total makeover
LOOK YOUNGER, FEEL GREAT

Compiled, edited and designed by
Merricks Media Ltd
3 & 4 Riverside Court
Lower Bristol Road
Bath, BA2 3DZ
Tel: 01225 786800
redguides@merricksmedia.co.uk
www.redguides.co.uk

Managing Editor Daphne Razazan
Editor Amy Lindsay
Assistant Editor Leaonne Hall
Researcher Melissa Ogden
Art Editor Bonnie Coupland
Design Angela Ashton
Production Editor Chrissy Williams
Managing Director Lisa Doerr
Publishing Director John Weir
Production Manager Graham Prichard
Advertising Manager Tina Blenkiron
Senior Sales Executive John Phillips
Advertisement Design Ruth Sargeson
Production Co-ordinator Ruth Sargeson

RED GUIDES is a trademark of Merricks Media Ltd

Cover image © **Goodshoot**
Copyright © **Merricks Media Ltd** 2005
Printed and bound in the UK by St Ives Roche.
ISBN 1-90504921-8 British Library Cataloguing in Publication Data.
First edition 2006.

A catalogue record for this bookazine is available from the British Library.

This version of **Total Makeover** is exclusive to WHSmith.

welcome

We all know that when we look good, we feel better. It's amazing what a slick of lipstick or dropping a dress size can do for our self-esteem and confidence. So these pages are crammed full of objective advice on all the latest products, treatments and lifestyle changes available to help you look and feel younger and healthier, and get you glowing inside and out.

We have approached experts in the fields of skincare, well-being and cosmetic surgery, so you'll find up-to-the-minute information on everything from anti-ageing 'Superfoods' and supplements to face lifts that iron out those stubborn frown lines. There should be something to suit everyone, regardless of your age, skin type or budget – and check out our handy grid on page 26 for a simple way to discover a treatment that will suit you.

Total Makeover is the UK's most authoritative guide to the current options available for a new, fabulous self-image. If you're thinking of a cosmetic surgery procedure or a lifestyle change, this guide will serve as your foolproof companion to how you can achieve it safely and effectively.

Read on and look forward to a radiant future, with a younger, healthier, happier you...

Enjoy!

Amy

AMY LINDSAY
Amy Lindsay is a health and beauty writer who has spent most of her career investigating the secrets of flat stomachs and radiant skin. Following a Postgraduate degree in magazine journalism, Amy has contributed to publications such as *Grazia* and the *Daily Mirror*, writing on everything from holiday health hazards to miracle make-up products.

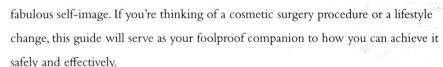

CONTENTS

46

153

132

32

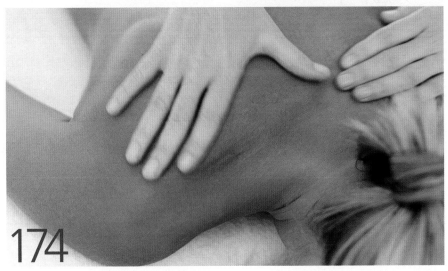
174

135

156

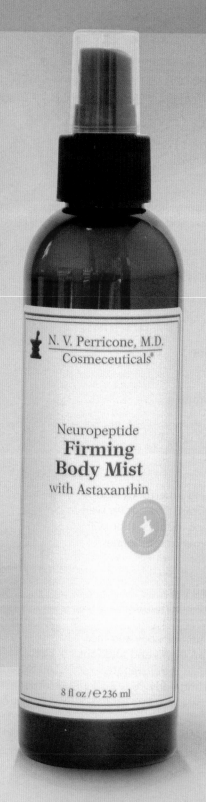

PANEL OF EXPERTS

MAIN CONTRIBUTORS

DR SARAH BREWER
Dr Sarah Brewer graduated from Cambridge University as a doctor in 1983. She was a full-time GP for five years and now works in nutritional medicine. She writes widely on all aspects of health, including integrative medicine and the sensible use of supplements. She has written over 40 popular self-help books and appears regularly on TV and radio. Sarah is currently completing a masters degree in Nutritional Medicine at the University of Surrey, Guildford. Sarah was voted Health Journalist of the Year 2002.

SUSANNAH MARRIOTT
Susannah Marriott is a freelance writer who specialises in complementary healthcare and natural beauty. She has written 12 books on yoga, meditation and spa treatments, including *Spice Spa*, *The Art of the Bath*, *Total Meditation* and *Basic Yoga*. Her latest title, *Your Non-Toxic Pregnancy*, shows how to replace potentially damaging products in your home with safe, natural alternatives. Before becoming an author, Susannah spent 12 years editing and managing complementary health books for Dorling Kindersley. Her work has appeared in *Weekend Guardian*, *Zest*, *Shape*, *Top Santé* and *Healthy*, and she has broadcast on BBC Radio 4. Susannah lives in Cornwall with her partner and three daughters.

EMMA WHITE
Emma White has written for several healthcare and medical publications, including freelance work for the *Daily Mail*'s Good Health section. Since graduating from St Andrews University and completing Cardiff University's Postgraduate diploma in magazine journalism, Emma has written about everything from beauty on a night out and hangover cures, to food allergies and arthritis.

COSMETIC DENTISTRY

DR MARK ALEXANDER HUGHES BA BDentSc HONS (DUBL)
Dr Mark Hughes is the principal dentist at his recently launched Harley Street Dental Studio. He graduated from Trinity College Dublin in 1992 with honours and is pursuing a Masters degree in restorative dentistry. Dr Hughes regularly attends international training courses and is a member of the American Academy of Cosmetic Dentistry and British Academy of Cosmetic Dentistry.

DR ANTHONY ZYBUTZ B.D.S
Dr Anthony Zybutz qualified from Wits dental school in Johannesburg, South Africa in 1992, with a Bachelor of Dental Surgery. He then designed, built and ran a four-surgery dental practice in central London before taking over the established Harley Street practice of his friend and mentor, the late Mr John Bunyan.

COSMETIC SURGERY

MR DAI DAVIES (FRCS)
Dai Davies has over 20 years' experience in aesthetic plastic surgery and specialises in facial and breast surgery. He is on the GMC's specialist register as a trained surgeon in plastic and reconstructive surgery, an FRCS examiner and has been a consultant and senior lecturer in plastic and reconstructive surgery at Hammersmith, Charing Cross and St Mary's hospitals. Previously, he was the honorary secretary to the British Association of Aesthetic Plastic Surgeons (BAAPS) and a member of the Court of Examiners of the Royal College of Surgeons, and is currently also a member of the British Association of Plastic Surgeons (BAPS), the British Hand Society and the International Society of Aesthetic Plastic Surgery. He also finds the time to act as an advisor to the Medical Protection Society.

DR LUCY GLANCEY
Dr Lucy Glancey specialises in cosmetic medicine using the latest treatments for surgical and non-surgical treatments such as laser therapy, Botox and collagen as well as cellulite and persistent fat removal. A member of the Royal College of Surgeons of England, the British Association of Cosmetic Doctors and the American Academy of Cosmetic Surgeons, Glancey lectures regularly to the beauty industry and other medical staff in the use of cosmetic procedures including the thread lift. As well as running cosmetic clinics in Essex and London, she also contributes to press interviews and television, including appearances on *10 Years Younger*, *GMTV* and *Celebrity Cosmetic Surgery*.

DR RAJIV GROVER
Rajiv Grover works as an NHS Consultant Plastic Surgeon as well as running a private practice in Harley Street and London's King Edward VII Hospital. He graduated in medicine in 1989 from London University and, after becoming a Fellow of the Royal College of Surgeons in 1993, went on to specialise in Plastic Surgery. During his training he was awarded an MD from the University of London and a Hunterian Professorship by the Royal College of Surgeons of England. Prior to becoming a consultant, he was awarded a scholarship in Plastic Surgery to Harvard Medical School in Boston, USA.

MS ANGELICA KAVOUNI, MD, FRCS
Angelica Kavouni completed her fellowship at the Institute of Plastic Surgery, Stamford Hospital. She heads a busy private practice, providing a complete range of cosmetic surgical interventions, although her passion lies in breast enhancement and facial surgery with skin rejuvenation. Clinic safety, excellence and confidentiality are of the utmost importance, as directed by the CareStandards Act and guidelines for Good Surgical Practice. Kavouni is on the GMC specialist register in Plastic Surgery and is a fellow of the European Boards in Plastic, Reconstructive and Aesthetic Surgery. She is also a member of the International Federation of Plastic, Reconstructive and Aesthetic Surgery (IPRAS).

MR LAURENCE KIRWAN (MD, FRCS)
British-born Laurence Kirwan has 20 years' experience in aesthetic plastic surgery and works between London and the US at his practices in Harley Street, London, New York's 5th Avenue and Connecticut. Kirwan, who specialises in facial and body surgery, is a Fellow of the Royal College of Surgeons, the American Society of Plastic Surgeons as well as of the American Society for Aesthetic Plastic Surgery. When in Connecticut, he also directs The Kirwan Skin Klinic, which offers a wide range of non-invasive procedures, the Kirwan Hair Transplant Centre and the Kirwan Vein Centre. In 1996, Kirwan was awarded a Professorship as a founding member of the International School for Aesthetic Plastic Surgery in Belgrade, Serbia.

MR JAN STANEK (FRCS)
Jan Stanek has been in his own practice for over 20 years. His speciality is in facial cosmetic surgery. He is also the surgeon of choice for the Channel 4 series *10 Years Younger*. Stanek travels widely to attend conferences and give lectures, particularly in the US. In his native country, the Czech Republic, he holds the posts of Visiting Professor in Aesthetic Plastic Surgery and Director for the Department of Experimental Plastic Surgery within the Faculty of Plastic and Reconstructive Surgery at the University of Brno, Czech Republic.

HAIR

ROYSTON BLYTHE AND NICK MALENKO
Dynamic duo Royston and Nick have been providing fantastic hairstyles and excellent customer service at their salon in Wolverhampton since 1989. Known for their drive and determination, they often take part in shows like Salon International and educational seminars at the L'Oréal Professional Academy.

GLENN LYONS
Glenn Lyons qualified as a trichologist in 1968, before being granted full membership of the Institute of Trichologists in 1971. He worked on the board of Governors and was responsible for the education of final year students. In 1971 Lyons was elected as a member of the Royal Institute of Public Health and Hygiene and the Society of Cosmetic Scientists, and in 1977 to the Royal Society of Medicine. The author of several published research projects, Lyons was also awarded 'The Fellowship of the Institute' in recognition of his work on female pattern hair loss. Lyons also finds time to appear on television and radio, and contribute to magazine articles.

TREVOR SORBIE
Pioneer of cuts and styling techniques such as The Wedge, The Chop and The Scrunch, as well as producing his own range of professional high street haircare products, Trevor Sorbie has won the coveted British Hairdresser of the Year title an unrivalled four times. Widely acknowledged as one of the best UK hairdressers, Sorbie is also fun-loving and unassuming. His diverse catalogue of TV credits range from *This Morning* to *Faking It*.

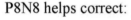

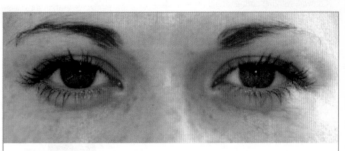

1

what can a makeover do for you?

INTRODUCTION

These days looking younger than your years can be easily achieved. There are a whole host of ways to make the most of what nature has given you, or even to reverse the ageing process, making you look younger and feel rejuvenated. One thing is for certain: the earlier you start to look after your skin, the better the results will be in later life.

look good,

Research carried out by the Body Beautiful cosmetic surgery in 2005 found that 45% of women would consider having cosmetic surgery, compared to just 22% contemplating procedures in 2004

feel good

IMPROVE THE WAY YOU FEEL AND LOOK

WITH THE AID OF MODERN technology, there are a multitude of ways to make yourself look younger. From anti-wrinkle creams to cosmetic surgery, the possibilities for changing your physical appearance are endless. However, experts stress that lifestyle plays a huge part in retaining your youthfulness: no number of miracle creams and health farm visits can substitute for a lifetime of good grooming and healthy lifestyle choices.

Looking younger is not only about appearing youthful on the outside. Any person who has undergone surgery stresses the psychological benefits of feeling younger on the inside. Patients say that confidence, happiness and a boost in self-esteem are well worth the price tag of an anti-ageing procedure. Self-image and self-confidence go hand in hand.

As time passes our looks will inevitably change, but now we can slow down (or even turn back) the clock to defy the signs of ageing and boost our feeling of well-being. If you're considering a cosmetic surgery procedure, you're not alone. Research carried out by the Body Beautiful cosmetic surgery in 2005 found that 45 per cent of women would consider having cosmetic surgery, compared to just 22 per cent contemplating procedures in 2004. And indeed, many more modern women are actually going under the knife. According to the British Association of Aesthetic Plastic Surgeons (BAAPS), the number of cosmetic surgery treatments undertaken by BAAPS members rose by 60 per cent in 2004. Figures by BUPA show that up to 75,000 procedures (both invasive and non-invasive) are performed every year in Britain, with 92 per cent being performed on women.

The anti-ageing cosmetics market is also booming. More than £6 million is spent on anti-ageing creams every year in the UK, and a recent report found that women use an average of 29 beauty products per day. It is estimated this sector will enjoy a further 8.5% growth by 2007 just with the increase of 'doctor brand' products, developed by dermatologists and surgeons to have more dramatic results.

Of course the underlying reason behind any change we make, from undergoing a cosmetic procedure to buying a new skin cream, comes from our desire to boost our own confidence and self-worth. There are many ways to improve the way you feel and look: read on to find out.

YOUR CHOICE

There are many different options you can turn to in order to start looking and feeling younger:
- skin creams and treatments
- non-invasive rejuvenation techniques
- cosmetic surgery
- changes to diet
- changes to lifestyle
- more exercise

GOODSHOOT

YOUR INTRODUCTION TO FEELING AND LOOKING YOUNGER >>

The secret to looking young is with

THE ANTI-AGEING CLINIC

- **Free Consultation**
- **Anti-wrinkle injections**
  (for further info visit www.botox.com)
- **Restylane/Perlane**
- **Isolagen**
- **AMELAN®** - Depigmentation (brown patches caused by ageing/pigmentation)
  - Facial Rejuvenation
- **Dermatology**

Dr M Mahmood

(MB ChB DFFP DPD BACD AAAAM)
Senior Partner in a NHS General Practice.
Registered with the General Medical Council,
a member of the British Association of
Cosmetic Doctors and The American
Academy of Anti-Aging Medicine.

Tel: **020 8989 9391** (24 hrs)
E-mail: **info@antiageing.co.uk**
Web: **www.antiageing.co.uk**

18 Chigwell Road, South Woodford
London E18 1LS

WHAT TO CONSIDER

With such a large choice of treatments and products, how do you decide which procedure will be best for you? This is not a simple question to answer, as your skin will have different needs in each stage of life and every woman's skin responds differently to treatments and creams: a miracle cure recommended by a friend may prove to have no effect on you. Similarly, it all depends on the results you desire and how much expense and discomfort you are willing to go through to get them. The most important part is to do your research and question the professionals. An experienced GP, dermatologist, cosmetic surgeon or even beauty counter assistant will have seen many people in the same quandary as yourself and – providing they are reputable – should be able to give you reliable, impartial advice on which treatment or product will be most suited to your skin type and deliver the results you want.

If you are unsure as to whether a lifestyle change, over-the-counter cream, non-invasive treatment or full cosmetic surgery procedure would be best for you, then read on as we explore all the options in some detail.

'An experienced GP, dermatologist, cosmetic surgeon or even beauty counter assistant will have seen many people in the same quandary as yourself and – providing they are reputable – should be able to give you reliable, impartial advice'

home. With very rare exceptions of an allergic reaction, skin creams and treatments should involve no discomfort or recovery time. Results will be subtle and gradually build over time.

Q And the drawbacks?
A If you opt for a skincare program to improve the age of your skin, the primary factor to consider is that this requires a consistent routine. Where other options are one-off treatments with long-lasting results, a skincare treatment must be maintained on a daily basis for at least a month for visible and sustainable results. As such, if you are investing in an expensive skincare routine, the costs may mount up over time. Skincare solutions are usually best for preventing early environmental damage (you'll need a cream with a 15+ sun protection factor) and protecting from future damage – very few can drastically reverse existing damage.

SKIN CREAMS & TREATMENTS

Q How effective are they?
A Skin products that are available over the counter can deliver pleasing results, but for something that works on a deeper level, you will need a cosmeceutical product (a biologically active product that combines skincare with science to deliver drug-like benefits). With all types of creams and DIY home treatments, the effectiveness of the product will depend on whether it is right for your skin type and whether you have used it correctly – always read the instructions carefully. Use products at least once or twice a day and expect to wait at least one month before there are any visible results.

Q What are the advantages, compared to other options?
A The obvious advantage with a skin cream or home treatment is that they are non-invasive and safe for you to use in the comfort of your own

Q What if it doesn't work?
A The best chance of a product working is if you have done some research and chosen wisely – a dermatologist should be able to advise you. If the cream or treatment does not work, the good news is that it will not have cost you vast amounts of money, so it is possible to experiment with different treatments until you find one that works for you.

'Skincare solutions are best for preventing early environmental damage (you'll need a cream with a 15+ sun protection factor) and protecting from future damage – very few can drastically reverse existing damage'

WHAT TREATMENT IS RIGHT FOR YOU?

To start with, below is a list of general questions you should ask yourself when choosing which type of treatment might be most suitable for you:

● How severe is the problem?
● How dramatic do I want the results to be?
● What is my budget?
● How much time can I take off for rest and recuperation?
● How will I need to prepare?
● Am I willing to keep up treatments to maintain results?
● How long do I want the results to last?
● Do I have any medical conditions to bear in mind?
● Does my skin scar or bruise easily?
● How well do I cope with pain?
● Does my blood clot healthily?
● Do I heal quickly?
● Do I want instant results?
● Do I want the option to reverse the result if I don't like it?

Care Dental

Featuring a well-established cosmetic dentist Mukesh Soni and his associates, Care Dental offers dentistry of an uncompromisingly high standard that is focused on the unique needs, total comfort, and ultimate satisfaction of each individual patient.

Dr Soni has placed over 1,000 implants!

Dr Soni trained under world-leading implantologists Dr Hilt Tatum and Dr Ashok Sethi. Dr Soni is also an active member of:

- Association of Dental Implantology
- American Academy of Cosmetic Dentistry
- British Society of Periodontology
- British Dental Association
- British Endodontic Society
- Royal College of Surgeons

2 Years 0% interest available today!*
*Terms and conditions apply

Call us today on 020 8570 2526 and book your FREE consultation

INVESTORS IN PEOPLE UK

Member
AMERICAN ACADEMY OF COSMETIC DENTISTRY®

Care Dental - 305 Bath Road - Hounslow - TW3 3DB
www.caredental.co.uk

>> SKIN CREAMS CASE STUDY

Sue, 48, has found the ideal skincare solution

Q Did you consider surgery?

A I have never liked the idea of surgery, as I have quite a low pain threshold and also suffer from high blood pressure, which makes many medical procedures impossible. I would also be very nervous to have something drastic done in case I did not like the results. As such, my anti-ageing routine revolves around skincare products that deliver subtle and gradual results over time.

Q Which products work best for you?

A I have tried many products, starting with cheaper brands such as Olay, and now I follow the NV Perricone Cosmeceutical skincare routine. Although the products are expensive, I see them as an investment in my skin and they are certainly cheaper than having regular non-invasive procedures or a face lift. I intend to keep up my routine to maintain the results as long as is necessary – people certainly say I look 10 years younger than I am!

NON-INVASIVE REJUVENATING TECHNIQUES

Q How safe is it?

A The non-invasive market is rapidly expanding, with new procedures cropping up all the time. As the popularity of non-invasive procedures grows, so does the proof of their safety: last year 50,000 Botox injections and 30,000 Restylane treatments were safely carried out in the UK. Although there have been well-documented celebrity disasters after procedures such as Botox and collagen lip injections, the truth is that such reactions are very rare and all procedures are well tested and monitored before they become widely available to the public. Likewise, any practitioner needs to have been thoroughly trained in a procedure before he is licensed to practise it. Many of the products used in non-invasive techniques are derived from traditional medical procedures, so come with the reputation of being safe to use. If you have any doubts at all, raise them with your practitioner who will be able to assure you that all products are safe and any risks are minimal.

Q What are the advantages, compared to cosmetic surgery?

A The obvious advantage of non-invasive techniques is that they do not involve extensive surgery and, as such, the pain involved, potential risks and necessary healing times are all much lower. Many non-invasive procedures can be done in your lunch hour, without requiring time off work or bearing any visible effects other than younger, brighter skin. Non-invasive procedures are also usually temporary, with results fading within a few months to a few years. If you do not like the results, you will not have to undergo

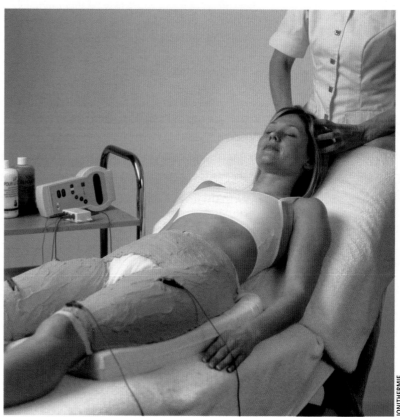

IONITHERMIE

Non-invasive procedures are a great option for those unwilling to commit to cosmetic surgery

further costly and potentially painful surgery to change them, as the results will disappear in time.

Q And the drawbacks?

A The drawbacks are that they can be costly and don't have lasting effects. Within a few months you may have to return for repeat procedures, which can be expensive compared to one-off surgery fees.

'Last year 50,000 Botox injections and 30,000 Restylane treatments were safely carried out in the UK'

>>

Many of the products on the non-invasive market are also quite new, so it is essential to find an experienced and well-trained practitioner to avoid adverse side effects.

Q What could go wrong?

A It is true that some individuals have rare allergic reactions to some of the ingredients in non-invasive products. However, the likelihood of this can be minimised by asking for an allergy test before undergoing a procedure. As non-invasive procedures are generally not permanent, any allergic reactions will fade in time. The initial after-effects of a procedure may be slight redness, bruising, swelling, itching or skin peeling but these will all fade within a matter of hours or days.

Q How regulated is it?

A As so many new non-invasive procedures are emerging all the time, it is difficult for regulators to keep on top of them. However, rest assured that practitioners would not want to put their reputation on the line by practising a procedure where they were not 100% assured that it was safe and effective. The Healthcare Commission anticipates that non-invasive procedures will be regulated by the end of 2006 and in the meantime can provide information on whether practitioners and clinics are legally registered: www. healthcarecommission.org.uk or 0845 601 3012.

Q How do I find a reliable practitioner?

A Both BAAPS (www.baaps.org.uk) and The Consulting Room (www.consultingroom.com) can help you to find a properly accredited surgeon or practitioner in your area who specialises in the procedure you want. If you still feel uncertain, you can also check up on the credentials of healthcare professionals providing non-surgical procedures on the Nursing and Midwifery Council (www. nmc-uk.org) as well as the General Dental Council (www.gdc-uk.org) websites.

>> NON-INVASIVE TREATMENTS CASE STUDY

Fiona, 38, decided her wrinkle lines were making her look older than her years

Q Why did you decide to have treatment?

A A few months ago I started a new job and began to notice how much younger all the other girls in the office were. Although I dress well and generally look after my appearance with a healthy diet and exercise, the fine lines and wrinkles on my face were becoming more pronounced and making me look older than I felt. I had heard about Botox and found a recommended clinic for a consultation. They said the injections would deliver temporary results, relaxing the muscles in my face to soften the frown lines. I didn't have to think twice and signed up immediately!

Q What was the treatment like?

A The injections were not painful and I was back at work within the hour. Although the results are only temporary, they are incredibly effective and I intend to maintain treatments to put off the inevitable for as long as possible.

FIND A SURGEON

As with non-invasive procedures, both BAAPS (www.baaps.org.uk) and The Consulting Room (www.consultingroom. com) can help you find a properly accredited surgeon in your area who specialises in the procedure you want. The British Association of Cosmetic Doctors (www.cosmeticdoctors. co.uk) also has details of reputable practitioners.

COSMETIC SURGERY

Q How safe is it?

A No surgeon or procedure is 100% risk-free; however, being informed on the procedure you are having and finding a reputable, experienced and qualified surgeon drastically decrease the chances of anything going wrong. There are few risks and multiple benefits to every procedure, so make sure you are fully aware of what to expect. Surgeons are obliged to inform you about any risks with a more than 1% chance of occurrence, so don't be scared off by statistics – the chances of things going wrong are usually very low, as all procedures have to be fully tried and tested before they are approved. For further information, look up the British Association of Aesthetic Plastic Surgeons'

(BAAPS) general safety guidelines for anyone considering aesthetic plastic surgery treatments at www.baaps.org.uk, or call their advice line on 020 7405 2234.

Q Is there an optimum age to do it?

A The optimum age varies with each individual and procedure. For example, a woman as young as 25 who has had children and completed her family may be the ideal candidate for a breast lift. On the whole, women between 35 and 50 are the most common candidates for cosmetic surgery (this age group makes up 46% of cosmetic surgery patients). By this age, gravity and environmental factors will have started to take their toll, so you will see good results. However, do bear in mind that the more elasticity your skin has, the better you will heal, so it is advisable not too leave it too late.

Q How long will the effects last?

A The effects of invasive cosmetic surgery procedures are, on the whole, permanent, so it is worth taking your time when deciding whether to undergo an operation, as it can be costly and painful to reverse procedures. Most results will last a lifetime, providing you follow the doctor's post-operation advice: having a tummy tuck then eating take-away food and chocolate every day can soon undo a surgeon's good work!

Q How do I find a surgeon?

A There is no substitute for having a skilled and experienced surgeon, so it is always worth shopping around when selecting one. Statistics show that 62% of people undergoing cosmetic procedures only have one consultation but it is always best to see at least two surgeons, preferably three or more before you make your selection – never underestimate the peace of mind that comes from having been able to compare and confirm the opinions of different medical professionals. A good starting point is the recommendation of friends, or to look at listings on sites such as the BAAPS site mentioned on the opposite page.

Q What should I ask?

A Most initial consultations cost between £75-£150 and take up to one hour. Make sure you use your time wisely by arriving with a list of pre-prepared questions. Below are some guidelines on important things to ask:

● Where will the procedure take place, and does the surgeon have an association with a particular hospital or clinic?

● Has the surgery been licensed by the local health authority?

● What are the basics of the procedure?

● What anaesthetic will be used?

● What are the risks and potential complications of the procedure? The practitioner has a professional obligation to tell you about complications with an incidence rate of more than 1%, so do not be too alarmed by the possible risks as they are generally very rare.

● How long will the procedure take?

● How long will the results last?

● How long will I take to heal? Where will the incisions – and therefore scars – be? How long will the bruising and swelling take to go down?

● How much time will I need off work? When will I be able to drive?

● If I don't like the result, what can be done?

● What are the alternatives?

Find out exactly what results you can expect from surgery

'Surgeons are obliged to inform you about any risks with a more than 1% chance of occurrence, so don't be scared off by statistics – the chances of things going wrong are usually very low'

Q What could go wrong?

A Your risks of surgical complications increase with age and will also vary according to how fit and well you are when you undertake the surgery. The rate of complications from well-executed surgery is very low but rare risks include haematoma (a collection of blood underneath the skin that needs to be drained – more common in smokers, people with high blood pressure and those who are too active post-surgery), raised or thickened scars, infections, nerve damage and even death. Be aware that complications are rare and ask your practitioner for statistics on the likelihood of things going wrong to set your mind at rest.

Q What if something does go wrong?

A Most complications will amend themselves over time. For example, scars will fade and settle down.

DO YOUR RESEARCH

Before scheduling a consultation with a surgeon, follow these tips to save yourself valuable time and money:

● Visit doctors' websites and request a brochure of their practice, as well as information on the procedure you are interested in.

● Ask other specialists and your GP for referrals and feel free to listen to recommendations from friends who have had work done.

● Make sure the surgeon is a reputable member of an organisation and that he has had extensive training and experience in performing the procedure you are considering (if the surgeon has trained in the UK, he should be listed in the General Medical Council Specialist Register: www.gmc-uk.org). Also look for the title 'Consultant Plastic Surgeon'.

● Find out in advance about the range of fees so you work out how feasible your budget is.

● Ask to see before/after images of patients the surgeon has performed the procedure on to get an idea of their skills and what results to expect.

Infections will be treated and any numbness will only be temporary. If you are not pleased with the results of surgery, then you will have some kind of recourse with a reputable surgeon. Most practitioners will be willing to revise the result at a reduced fee or no charge, although you will usually have to pay hospital and anaesthetist fees. Before you do have repeat surgery, you must wait for the original healing process to be complete, which may take 6-12 months, as the tissues must be fully healed. Be aware that the chances of risks occurring increase with each procedure.

DIET & LIFESTYLE OPTIONS

Q What options are there?
A Environmental and lifestyle factors have a big impact on the skin. Smoking, drinking, damaging free radicals in the environment, sun exposure

'Cutting down on the amount you drink will also benefit the skin as alcohol dehydrates the skin, leaving it looking dry and sallow'

and stress all have a detrimental effect on your skin so it is important to lead a lifestyle that omits as many of these damaging elements as possible. Dermatologists and cosmetic surgeons would always advise smokers to quit as – in addition to increasing the risk of heart disease and cancer – smoking reduces blood flow to the skin, causing an increase in wrinkles and a dull complexion. Cutting down on the amount you drink will also benefit the skin as alcohol dehydrates the skin, leaving it looking dry and sallow. Wearing a high sun protection factor (15+) will protect skin

from harmful UV rays, forming a protective layer against the ageing damage of the sun. Other ways to lead a youthful lifestyle are to follow diets that recommend skin-boosting foods and supplements, to drink plenty of water to keep skin hydrated, to exercise, sleep well and take time to relax.

Q How effective are they?
A It is well-known that no number of skincare creams or operations can deliver the same benefits to your body as a healthy lifestyle. A life free from sun damage, stress, smoking and alcohol will leave your body healthy on the inside, which is reflected on the outside. What you eat, the way you live and how you exercise will affect the way you feel and the age you look. By following a healthy lifestyle, you will rejuvenate and restore your inner and outer youthfulness.

Q What are the advantages, compared to other options?
A The obvious advantage is that lifestyle change costs nothing and presents no risks to your health. In fact, it positively boosts your health and well-being. It's never too late to start and the sooner you do, the longer the anti-ageing benefits will last.

Q And the drawbacks?
A It is better to undertake lifestyle changes earlier in life as a preventative measure. Although stopping smoking, taking up exercise, wearing sun cream and eating healthily are always good changes to make to your lifestyle, they are not so effective at reversing damage that has already been done. In younger years, a healthy diet and lifestyle will be enough alone to maintain youthfulness, but once you are older, these changes may need to be combined with other options, such as a treatment or cream, to boost the benefits.

>> DIET CASE STUDY

Jean, 42, chose to change her lifestyle rather than have cosmetic surgery

Q How did you decide to change your lifestyle?
A As I hit my forties, I started to notice my skin was looking sallow and saggy and no amount of creams was helping nature. I began to consider cosmetic surgery but decided I could neither afford the fees nor the time off. I started looking into more holistic ways to boost my skin. Within a matter of weeks, I cut out all refined sugar, processed foods, fatty snacks and bloating carbohydrates such as white bread from my diet. I made sure I

was drinking at least two litres of water a day and getting all the recommended vitamins and minerals I needed.

Q What were the results?
A Within weeks, I found my energy levels were boosted, my skin was glowing and I was sleeping so much better. Although changing my lifestyle hasn't given me the results overnight, I know they will be sustainable.

WHAT HAPPENS TO YOUR FACE AND BODY AS YOU AGE?

The skin we inherited from our parents, what we have exposed it to and how we have looked after it will all affect how profoundly and quickly we age. However, there are certain inevitables that nature has in store. Our hair will turn grey and we will all experience skin becoming thinner as we lose facial fat. Our skin will wrinkle and sag and will lose its ability to retain moisture, showing the signs of damage caused by years of exposure to the sun and environment.

20s

By the time most women hit 20, their skin is in its prime, so a skincare routine is all about prevention rather than cure.

You've survived the teenage years of spots, your pores should be invisible and your skin blemish-free. Skin should be even in tone, smooth and taut. However, it's essential not to take good skin for granted!

Make sure you eat a well-balanced diet, drink plenty of fluids and take regular exercise to keep skin looking rosy and hydrated. It is also essential to start – and maintain – a regular skincare routine. You need to moisturise daily, with a light moisturiser that contains a high sun protection factor (factor 15+) to prevent sun damage, and you should exfoliate skin once a week to remove dead cells which may clog your pores.

A healthy, active lifestyle in your twenties with regular exercise will also delay the accumulation of fat in later decades.

30s

During your thirties, you will begin to see the first signs of ageing. These will usually be subtle changes, such as thinning skin under your eyes which leaves puffy dark circles under your eyes after a late night.

Looking good in your thirties takes more time and effort than it did at 21, and requires a systematic program of maintenance. If you're starting to notice fine lines, wrinkles and discolouration, it's time to boost your skincare regimen and perhaps upgrade your make-up routine. Make sure you keep your skin well hydrated, especially during winter months, by drinking plenty of fluid and using a heavier moisturiser with a high sun protection factor. You may need to use a night cream in the evenings if your skin still feels dry and an eye cream during the day to keep the skin around the eyes looking tight and bright.

Your thirties is a good time to start trying out anti-ageing formulas.

40s

During your forties, you will see noticeable changes in your skin's tone and texture. Your skin will no longer be as tight as it used to be, and it may appear dull with large, visible pores. It is also in this decade that you can expect to see signs of sun damage if you have not been using the right protective creams. These signs may include blotches, freckles, age spots, discolouration, and changes in skin colour. If these symptoms are very apparent, it may be worth adding products that lighten dark spots to your daily skincare routine to even out your skin tone.

Your skin may feel dryer than in previous decades, so be sure to explore the vast array of anti-ageing products available. You can reinvigorate tired skin with firming treatments that visibly improve firmness and texture.

Most women start to look at non-invasive options for anti-ageing during this decade.

50s

By your sixth decade the ageing process is in high gear, and you will experience a loss of volume and fullness, leaving loose, sagging skin. The change in hormone production levels will also have dramatic effects on the skin. The level of oestrogen in your skin will diminish, leaving skin looking less soft, supple and hydrated.

Additional changes that may appear with the onset of menopause are the over-production of oil, enlarged pores and facial hair growth due to the presence of testosterone. Regular facials with massage can help increase the skin's circulation. DIY firming masks and hydrating treatments with mild exfoliation will also help to rejuvenate the skin's appearance. Ensure you take appropriate precautions against sun damage and continue to use products to help you stay moisturised.

Many women start to look at surgical options during this decade.

60s

The skin changes that you experience in your fifties will continue throughout your sixties, seventies and beyond.

By now, your skin will be loose, often resulting in jowls around the neck and loose skin on the stomach. The skin takes on a lighter colour due to poorer, decreased circulation, and the results of cumulative sun exposure will be apparent.

These changes are all part of the normal ageing process, and genetics as well as lifestyle factors play an important role in determining how well you will age. The better care you take of your skin in your thirties, forties and fifties, the better your skin will look in the sixties and beyond. It is at this point that a life-long use of high sun protection factor creams, a healthy diet, plenty of fluids and regular exercise will show their true worth. It's never too late to start taking care of yourself, and the earlier you start, the better.

>>

FIND A QUICK FIX

In the pages that follow, we round up some of the most common problems that can occur and come up with some quick fix solutions to rejuvenate your face and body and boost your sense of well-being

YOUR SKIN

PROBLEM: SAGGING SKIN

As your skin ages, the layer of fat under your skin that provides insulation and padding thins. This allows skin to sag and lose its structure as gravity pulls it down, while also increasing your risk of blood vessels breaking under the skin.

 **QUICK FIX**

To boost your skin's radiance, try investing in some of the wonderful skincare products on the market – especially those that are good for plumping, toning and tightening your skin.

PROBLEM: THINNING SKIN

With ageing, the outer layer of the skin (epidermis) becomes thinner, particularly around the eyes, so you may be able to see veins through the skin. Ageing skin may also appear paler and more translucent, with large pigmented spots (known as age or liver spots) appearing in sun-exposed areas. Simultaneously, the blood vessels of the dermis become more fragile, which leads to more noticeable bruising and potential bleeding under the skin, appearing in the form of small red lines.

 **QUICK FIX**

To disguise such blemishes on the surface of the skin, opt for a sheer, light-reflecting foundation which makes your skin look more dewy and youthful while diverting attention from blemishes and fine lines.

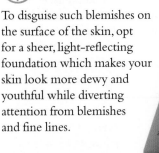

PROBLEM: DRY SKIN

The body produces less oil as you age, particularly after the menopause. This can make it much harder to keep the skin moist, resulting in dry, itchy or flaky skin with much more noticeable fine lines and wrinkles.

 **QUICK FIX**

To keep skin smooth, moisturise from inside and out, by investing in a good skin cream and ensuring you drink the recommended two litres of water a day.

PROBLEM: LOSS OF ELASTICITY

As we age, changes in the connective tissue reduce the skin's strength and elasticity. As a result of our body's reduced production of collagen fibres which give support to the skin, and elastin fibres which provide it with flexibility and strength, our skin becomes loose and sallow, losing its youthful plumpness and radiance.

 **QUICK FIX**

Boost your skin's radiance with an anti-ageing diet. Throw out all the processed and fatty foods and switch to nutrient-rich options to give you a boost inside and out.

PROBLEM: WRINKLES

Lines and wrinkles become more visible as we age, due to the looseness of the skin and also to repeated muscle contractions over time. Wrinkles on the forehead, on the bridge of the nose, and around the eyes and mouth are all due to repeated facial expressions over the years.

 **QUICK FIX**

To counter these expressions, try some of the facial exercises we outline later in this guide. They are quick and simple and can be carried out in the comfort of your own home.

SUN DAMAGE

● According to consultant dermatologist Dr Nick Lowe, about 30% of facial ageing is genetic and the rest is due to repetitive exposure to sunlight, smoking and other things such as damaging free radicals in the environment, poor nutrition and alcohol consumption.

● The greatest single factor that contributes to skin ageing is undoubtedly sun exposure, which can cause elastosis (loss of elasticity), thickening of the skin and pigment changes such as liver spots, not to mention the increased risk of cancer.

● Because most skin changes are related to sun exposure, prevention is a lifelong process. You should start preventing sunburn by wearing cream with a sun protection factor of 15+, wearing protective clothing in the sun and staying out of the harmful sun's rays as much as possible.

● Good nutrition, skincare routines, exercise and hydration habits are also good to develop while young as a preventative measure. However, once you are older, it is never too late to get into good habits. For more on sun protection see page 37.

PROBLEM: SLUGGISH CIRCULATION

As we age, our circulation also becomes less efficient. The blood pumps round our body at a much slower rate, so our skin does not get such a plentiful supply of nutrients as when we were younger. The effects of slower circulation are unsightly bags under the eyes and the accumulation of cellulite on the lower body. Thread veins may also appear on the legs (in the form of red squiggly lines) as blood is not being pumped around the body quite so efficiently.

 **QUICK FIX**

This can be remedied through exercise, which causes the heart rate to rise, encouraging the body to pump blood faster to boost our circulation as well as giving us an energy boost and calorie-burning workout.

'As we age, our circulation becomes less efficient. The blood pumps round our body at a slower rate, so our skin does not get as many nutrients'

FACE & NECK

As in the rest of the body, the typical appearance of the face and neck changes with age. Muscle tone may be lost, causing a flabby or droopy appearance and there may also be an increase in the number, size, and colour of pigmented spots on the face due to sun exposure. Although wrinkles are inevitable to some extent, sun exposure and cigarette smoke are likely to make them develop even faster.

PROBLEM: EYES

The eyebrows and eyelashes may become grey. The skin around the eyelids becomes loose and wrinkled, causing crow's feet to appear. The eye socket loses some of its fat pads, making the eyes look sunken and the eyebrows may droop. The lower eyelids may appear baggy, and drooping or sagging eyelids are fairly common. Poor circulation can lead to bags and dark circles under the eyes.

 **QUICK FIX**

To keep eyes looking moist and dewy, make-up artists advise investing in eye colours that are sheer but not shimmery. Use a slate or brown eyeliner to make eyes appear bigger and always apply mascara to disguise grey lashes. Also invest in a good concealer to disguise those under eye bags.

PROBLEM: CHIN AND JAWLINE

The jowls may begin to sag, contributing to a double chin and loose, sagging skin on the throat. The jawbone loses bone material, reducing the size of the lower face. The forehead and nose thus look more pronounced.

 **QUICK FIX**

Try some facial toning exercises to tighten up the chin and jawline: a few repetitions each day will deliver results. Alternatively, a decorative scarf or roll-neck jumper can quickly disguise a multitude of flaws.

It is important to keep your skin protected from the sun

PROBLEM: FOREHEAD

Deep expression lines (also known as frown lines) appear on the forehead and between the eyebrows. A loss of elasticity and fat in the skin may also cause the forehead to sag, causing your brows to look more 'hooded'.

 **QUICK FIX**

Again, facial exercises can help. Alternatively, a soft hairstyle that sweeps over the forehead or a pretty summer hat can hide wrinkles and also flatter your face. The hat will also prevent additional damaging sun exposure.

PROBLEM: CHEEKS

As we lose fat in the face, the cheeks will sag and may appear hollow or sunken. It is also common for thread veins to arise in the cheek area.

 **QUICK FIX**

A brush of blush breathes life into tired complexions while adding shading and contours. Experts recommend youthful warm apricot or rose shades.

PROBLEM: LIPS AND MOUTH

Lips tend to lose volume and become thinner as we age. Gums may also recede, contributing to dental problems and changes in the appearance of the mouth, as loss of teeth can make the lips look shrunken. Expression lines (caused by years of creating the same facial expressions) also appear around the mouth (oral commisures), at the grooves at the corners of the mouth (perioral lines) and between the nose and edge of the mouth (nasolabial lines).

QUICK FIX

Make-up artists recommend outlining lips with a creamy, soft lip pencil to make them appear full and natural. Find a sheer, moisturising lipstick to add volume to your pout.

BODY

Many people are concerned with changes in their body shape as they age. The human body is made up of fat, lean tissue (muscles and organs), bones, water, and other substances. As we age, the amount and distribution of these materials will change, causing our figure to alter. Although some changes inevitably occur with ageing, your lifestyle choices may slow or accelerate these changes.

PROBLEM: INCREASE IN FAT ON STOMACH, BOTTOM AND THIGHS

With age, fat tissue may become increasingly deposited at the centre of the body, particularly around the stomach area. The proportion of body fat may also increase by as much as 30%. However, after the age of 65, women will actually begin to lose weight as their amount of muscle tissue decreases. Of course, weight loss or gain will vary from person to person.

 **QUICK FIX**

A change in diet can help you to maintain a steady body weight. Cutting down on salty, fatty, sugary processed foods and opting for 'superfoods' will give you a boost inside and out and help to keep your weight stable.

PROBLEM: DECREASE IN LEAN BODY MASS

As fat increases, lean body mass decreases. Your muscles may lose some of their cells, bones may lose some of their minerals and become less dense, and tissue loss will reduce the amount of water in your body.

QUICK FIX

Exercise is a great way of building your muscle mass to keep muscles and bones strong. Just 30 minutes of light exercise three times a week will give great benefits and boost your mood too. Make sure you drink two litres of fluid a day to avoid dehydration, especially when exercising.

PROBLEM: CELLULITE

A reduction in your total body water as you age may make you more likely to get dehydrated. Dehydrated skin is dull and more prone to cellulite (fatty deposits under the skin that usually occur on the thighs, bottom and stomach).

 **QUICK FIX**

Drinking the recommended two litres of fluid per day will not only keep you hydrated, it will also help to flush the toxins out of your system to reduce cellulite and keep you looking and feeling energised.

PROBLEM: SAGGING LOOSE SKIN

As your skin loses elasticity, it is common for areas with excess skin to give in to the laws of gravity. Most commonly, breasts, upper arms, stomachs and bottoms will appear saggy, with loose skin.

Again, diet and exercise can boost the elasticity of the skin to make you look and feel more youthful, toned and supple. As an even quicker fix, invest in some supportive underwear, which can boost your breasts and hold in your buttocks to make you appear more perky.

'Diet and exercise can boost the elasticity of the skin to make you look and feel more youthful, toned and supple'

PROBLEM: THREAD VEINS

With circulation becoming more sluggish, it is not uncommon for thread veins to appear on the legs. Thread veins are the small red lines that appear on the surface of the skin and are caused by factors such as over-exposure to sunlight, pregnancy or over-exercising. As we become older, thin fragile veins may become weak due to prolonged pressure, causing blood to leak into the veins, blocking them and causing congestion. The thread veins will show up on the surface of the skin as tiny, string-like lines where the blood blockages occur. They are not dangerous or painful, merely unsightly.

Avoiding wearing skirts or investing in patterned tights is a good short-term remedy to distract from thread veins. Doing regular, gentle exercise also helps.

Diet and exercise are the key to keeping your body in shape

PROBLEM: AGEING HANDS

As we become older, our hands are often one of the first features to give away our age. As with the face, the skin on the hands has been exposed to harmful rays and environmental factors more than most areas on the body, which can result in hands appearing wrinkled with liver or age spots. A lack of moisture and thinning skin will also make the skin on the hands appear looser, with more prominent veins. A lack of nutrients may also leave nails brittle and ridged.

Invest in a good quality hand cream with a high sun protection factor: it is as essential to moisturise your hands as it is your face. Treat yourself to a manicure to deliver necessary oils and a splash of colour to dry, dull nails.

Although many age-related changes cannot be prevented, you can take certain steps to help slow or reduce them. These steps include exercising and eating healthily, while avoiding smoking, sun damage and excessive alcohol consumption, which all accelerate the visible signs of ageing. Remember: these changes do not necessarily happen to everyone, as lifestyle plays a large role in how fast these age-related changes take place. Once the damage has been done, try out the quick fix solutions above for an instant boost, or explore the multiple solutions in the pages that follow to see how you can permanently create a younger-looking, happier and more confident you.

TOP TIPS

We can all suffer from dry skin, particularly on our hands. Dry skin occurs when our cells have a poor ratio of keratin and water, causing the cells to flake. Top tips are:
- Rinse your hands thoroughly to avoid the build up of soap
- Exercise: this increases the flow of blood, nutrients and oxygen to your skin
- Avoid too many steam baths which leach moisture from your skin

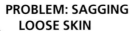

SOLVE YOUR PROBLEM

		DIET	LIFESTYLE & EXERCISE
SKIN	**FINE LINES AND WRINKLES**	Superfoods, co-enzyme Q10 supplement, vitamin A and related carotenoids	Sun screen, avoid smoking Exercise: facial exercises
	DEEP LINES AND WRINKLES	Superfoods, fish oils, vitamin A and related carotenoids	Sun screen, avoid smoking Exercise: facial exercises
	SUN DAMAGE	Lycopene, selenium	Wear high sun protection factor (SPF) sun screen
	DISCOLOURATION OR LIVER SPOTS	Lycopene, selenium	Wear high sun protection factor cream, blemish-concealing make-up
	BROKEN BLOOD VESSELS	Pycnogenol, isoflavones	Avoid smoking and excessive alcohol consumption. Holistic treatments (reiki / acupuncture) to improve blood flow to the skin
	DULL SKIN	Superfoods, evening primrose oil, fish oils, milk thistle Drink recommended two litres of fluid per day	Exercise: any exercise will boost circulation and improve the appearance of the skin
	SCARS OR STRETCH MARKS	Pycnogenol, vitamin E	Blemish-concealing make-up Holistic massage, plus reiki and acupuncture
	LOOSE, SAGGY SKIN	Superfoods, evening primrose oil, vitamin C, vitamin E	Exercise: toning and firming exercises
FACE	**CROW'S FEET AROUND THE EYES**	Grape seed extract, lutein, vitamin A and related carotenoids	Sunscreen around the eyes, wear sunglasses when in the sun Exercise: facial exercises

As an easy and accessible way to find the possible solutions to your problem, the grids in these pages outline the potential face and body problems you may wish to address down one side (categorised as skin, face and body) and possible solutions (categorised as diet/supplements, lifestyle & exercise, skin creams & treatments, non-invasive, surgery) along the top

SKIN CREAMS & TREATMENTS	NON-INVASIVE TREATMENTS	SURGERY
Creams or formulas containing co-enzyme Q10, vitamin C, acetyl hexapeptide-3 / argireline, DMAE (dimethylaminoethanol), gaba / gamma-amino-butyric acid or hexapeptide	Light therapy, temporary fillers, mesotherapy, thermage, chemical peel, IPL	Face lift, thread lift
Specialist skincare creams (cosmeceuticals), especially creams and formulas containing vitamin C, acetyl hexapeptide-3 / argireline, DMAE (dimethylaminoethanol), gaba / gamma-amino-butyric acid, hexapeptide or microdermabrasion	Permanent fillers, semi-permanent fillers, Botox, Isolagen, fat transfer, micro-current machines, chemical peel	Face lift, thread lift
Any skin cream with SPF of 15+, creams containing vitamin C, lycopene, niacinamide (nicotinamide), superoxide dismutase or vitamin E, P8N8 Skincare	Chemical peel, fraxel laser	Laser resurfacing
Skin creams with high SPF containing vitamin C, lycopene, niacinamide (nicotinamide), vitamin E or superoxide dismutase	IPL, thermage	Laser resurfacing
None	Veinwave, sclerotherapy	Spider vein removal
Radiance boosting skin creams, microdermabrasion, creams that contain alpha and beta hydroxy acids, panthenol, vitamin C or copper peptides	Mesolift, Purelogicol	Laser resurfacing
Products containing hyaluronic acid, retin A, vitamin A or vitamin E	Beautytek	Laser resurfacing
Firming and toning skin creams containing hyaluron, retin A, tazarotene, vitamin C or vitamin A	Thermage, micro-current machines, Perfector	PUAL-assisted lipoplasty (for body), face lift (for face)
Eye creams with furfuryladenine, DMAE (dimethylaminoethanol), acetyl hexapeptide-3 / argireline, gaba / gamma-amino-butyric acid, hexapeptide or vitamin A	Mesolift	Face lift, brow lift

	DIET	LIFESTYLE & EXERCISE
FACE — SAGGING, DROOPY EYELIDS	Grape seed extract, lutein, reishi, vitamin A and related carotenoids	Ensure you have adequate sleep each night Exercise: facial exercises
DARK CIRCLES AND BAGS UNDER THE EYES	Alpha-lipoic acid supplement, lutein, reishi, vitamin A and related carotenoids	Skin camouflage make-up, sleep Exercise: yoga to promote sleep
SAGGING JAWLINE	Evening primrose oil, vitamin E	Avoid extreme weight gain / loss Exercise: facial exercises
JOWLS / DOUBLE CHIN	Vitamin C, vitamin E	Avoid sudden weight gain / loss Exercise: facial exercises
THIN LIPS	Vitamin C, vitamin E	Avoid smoking and have regular dental check-ups to avoid disintegrating gums Exercise: none
LINES AROUND THE MOUTH (ORAL COMMISURES)	Vitamin C, vitamin E	Cutting out smoking – the most common cause of these lines Exercise: facial exercises
LINES BETWEEN NOSE AND EDGE OF MOUTH (NASOLABIAL LINES)	Vitamin C, vitamin E	Avoid smoking Exercise: facial exercises
FROWN LINES ON THE FOREHEAD OR BETWEEN EYEBROWS	Vitamin C, vitamin E	Avoid excessive frowning, get adequate sleep Exercise: facial exercises
SAGGING, SUNKEN, HOLLOW CHEEKS	Superfoods, vitamin C, vitamin E	Exercise: facial exercises
THREAD VEINS ON THE FACE	Pycnogenol, grape seed extract, isoflavones	Exercise: any exercise that boosts the heart rate to improve circulation
BODY — SAGGING BREASTS	Evening primrose oil, vitamin E	Wearing supportive underwear, good posture. Exercise: chest toning exercises
SMALL, EMPTY BREASTS	Vitamin C	Good posture will help breasts appear larger, supportive underwear Exercise: chest toning exercises

SKIN CREAMS & TREATMENTS	NON-INVASIVE TREATMENTS	SURGERY
Products containing hyaluron, vitamin A, vitamin C or retin A	Thermage	Blepharoplasty (upper eyelid surgery)
Intensive eye cream containing hyaluronic acid, retin A or vitamin A	Purelogicol	Blepharoplasty (eyebag / lower eyelid surgery)
Products containing tazarotene or vitamin A	Thermage	Lower face lift
Products containing tazarotene, vitamin C or vitamin E	Perfector, chin and cheek fillers	Chin tuck, neck lift
Products containing hyaluron, retin A, vitamins A, C or E	Temporary fillers to plump out lips	Lip augmentation
Creams containing furfuryladenine, gaba / gamma-amino-butyric acid, hexapeptide, vitamin C or vitamin E	Temporary fillers, semi-permanent fillers	Face lift
Those that contain DMAE (dimethylaminoethanol), acetyl hexapeptide-3 / argireline, gaba / gamma-amino-butyric acid, hexapeptide, vitamin C or vitamin E	Temporary fillers, semi-permanent fillers, Botox	Face lift
Those that contain DMAE (dimethylaminoethanol), acetyl hexapeptide-3 / argireline, gaba / gamma-amino-butyric acid, hexapeptide, vitamin C or vitamin E	Botox, fillers	Brow lift
Formulas containing hyaluron, retin A, vitamins A, C or E	Semi-permanent / permanent fillers to plump out cheeks	Cheek implants
None	Veinwave, IPL	Spider vein removal
Firming creams / gels containing alpha and beta hydroxy acids, hyaluron, vitamin A or vitamin C	Brava	Mastoplexy (breast lift)
Breast-boosting creams or gels containing hyaluron, retin A, vitamin A, vitamin C	Brava	Breast augmentation

BODY		DIET	LIFESTYLE & EXERCISE
	LARGE, PENDULOUS BREASTS	Vitamin E (to help relieve any breast pain)	Supportive underwear, good posture Exercise: chest, shoulder and back strengthening exercises
	SAGGING STOMACH	Evening primrose oil	Exercise: yoga, pilates, sit-ups to tone and cardiovascular exercise to burn calories
	POT BELLY	Superfoods, green tea Avoid bloating foods	Exercise: stomach toning exercises, pilates, yoga
	FAT BOTTOM	Acetyl-l-carnitine supplement, green tea	Exercise: bottom toning exercises and regular cardiovascular exercise to raise the heart rate and burn calories
	SAGGING BUTTOCKS	Vitamin C	Exercise: regular bottom toning exercises, yoga
	CELLULITE	Green tea, grape seed extract, isoflavones	Massage can help to break down fatty deposits under the skin. Light aerobic exercise using the legs will help to tone them and the improved circulation will break down cellulite
	FATTY THIGHS	Acetyl-l-carnitine supplement, green tea	Exercise: regular cardiovascular exercise to burn calories and leg toning exercises
	SPIDER OR THREAD VEINS ON LEGS	Pycnogenol, grape seed extract, isoflavones, reishi	Avoid smoking and excessive alcohol consumption. Exercise: cardiovascular exercise to boost circulation
	LOOSE, WRINKLED SKIN ON HANDS	Grape seed extract, isoflavones, vitamin C, vitamin E	Wear a high SPF on the hands
	PIGMENTED SKIN ON HANDS	Superfoods, lycopene, selenium	Wear a high SPF on the hands

SKIN CREAMS & TREATMENTS	NON-INVASIVE TREATMENTS	SURGERY
Firming or toning creams / gels containing vitamin E	Purelogicol (to improve skin firmness and elasticity)	Mammaplasty (breast reduction)
Firming creams containing alpha and beta hydroxy acids or vitamin A	Ionithermie, Ultrashape	Abdominoplasty (tummy tuck)
Body scrubs and creams containing green tea or caffeine	Ionithermie	Mini tummy tuck
A body wrap or firming cream containing green tea or caffeine	Ionithermie	Liposuction or buttock lift
Bottom toning / firming cream containing alpha and beta hydroxy acids, vitamin A or vitamin C	Mesotherapy	Buttock lift or buttock implants
Cellulite reducing gel containing green tea, grape seed extract, caffeine or vitamin A	Beautytek, VelaSmooth	Liposuction or liposelection using PUAL
A body toning wrap treatment or toning cream / gel containing green tea, caffeine or vitamin A	VelaSmooth, Beautytek	Liposuction or thigh lift
Formulas containing grape seed extract, vitamin A or vitamin E	Sclerotherapy, vasculight	Spider vein removal
Intensive hand treatment cream (with SPF) containing alpha and beta hydroxy acids, alphalipoic acid, hyaluron, retin A or tazarotene	Isolagen, fillers	Fat transfer (removing excess fat from another area of the body and injecting it into the hands)
Creams with retin A, vitamin A, alphalipoic acid, lycopene, niacinamide (nicotinamide), vitamin E or superoxide dismutase	Chemical peel, microdermabrasion	Laser resurfacing

2

the skin

CREAMS AND TREATMENTS

In the modern cosmetics market, there is a plethora of creams, scrubs, masks and patches that promise to take years off your appearance and make wrinkles disappear miraculously. Most come with a hefty price tag, making it difficult to decide which ones to invest in. Here we try and test the main contenders on the market to find out which ones are worth buying, and which ingredients will provide the best anti-ageing benefits for your skin.

In the last five years, the price women are prepared to pay for face cream has grown by an incredible 991%

Skin deep
CREAMS AND TREATMENTS

WITH AGE, THE SKIN'S NATURAL cell renewal process becomes less efficient, meaning that wrinkles increase and the skin loses its firmness. Every cosmetics counter is filled with products that promise to amend or reverse this deficiency with miracle-giving youth creams. The market grows annually as new formulas and ingredients are discovered, and recent research carried out by Olay shows that in the last five years, the price women are prepared to pay for face cream has grown by an incredible 991%.

CARE AT HOME

The main types of product in the anti-ageing market can be split into two groups: DIY (do-it-yourself) concentrated home treatment kits and BIY (buy-it-yourself) less intensive creams and formulas that you can buy over the counter.

DIY kits are a relatively new addition to the market, and usually take the form of masks and scrubs that claim to deliver the same results as a salon treatment. Many of these are based on the principle of facials or other fairly intensive treatments which are far more involved than the BIY creams. The BIY products are numerous and more varied, and are split into categories

either for the face as a whole, or products that focus on one specific problem area, such as eyes, lips, neck, throat or even the hands. These products come in new formats all the time. Although once all we had were simple creams, formulas now come as gels, patches, masks and scrubs. Products are also separated into day and night products. Daytime products are often thinner, designed to be worn underneath make-up and night creams are usually made of a slightly thicker, richer formula to be worn overnight for a more intensive result.

DO IT YOURSELF vs BUY IT YOURSELF

DIY (Do-it-yourself) kits claim to be as good as a salon treatment. Some examples are:
- a microdermabrasion treatment that will resurface your skin, and can take the form of a face peel
- intensive wrinkle-fixers – serums that are applied as a face mask

BIY (Buy-it-yourself) are less intensive treatments that tend to focus on a single area, for example:
- moisturising skin creams
- rejuvenating night creams

GOOD-NATURED

The most popular natural, botanical ingredients are:

- pomegranate
- grapefruit extract
- liquorice extract
- calendula
- aloe vera
- echinacea
- green tea
- ginkgo biloba

NATURAL INGREDIENTS

Skincare is not only using traditional, natural ingredients but is now also borrowing from medicine and surgery, taking the best new advances and ingredients and turning them into 'hope in a jar' formulas. Rejuvenating creams and treatments use both natural, botanical ingredients and synthetically produced moisturising ingredients in order to bring skin closer to looking 10 years younger. The most popular botanical ingredients are pomegranate, grapefruit and liquorice extracts, calendula, aloe vera, echinacea, green tea and ginkgo biloba. Most of these have been used throughout history as natural remedies to boost hydration and reduce irritation or inflammation in the skin. They are also known to have sun protection, age-reversal and anti-oxidant properties, protecting the skin against the damaging effects of the environment. More recently, a new breed of 'cosmeceuticals' has sprung up on the market. These are cosmetic products that use pharmaceutical technology to create creams and treatments with synthetic ingredients that should make the skin appear more youthful.

> 'While the average spend in Harrods beauty hall is a staggering £150, it seems that a face cream need not cost the earth to rejuvenate the skin'

However, these all come with a price tag. It is possible to spend from £3–£300 on a face cream, but the most important factor in finding an effective product is discovering one with the right ingredients that work for your skin, rather than the one that will do the most damage to your credit card. In his book 'Away With Wrinkles' dermatologist Dr Nick Lowe stresses that pricey products may not necessarily be the best ones for your skin. While the average spend in Harrods beauty hall is a staggering £150, it seems that a face cream need not cost the earth to rejuvenate the skin. 'Bear in mind that more expensive does not necessarily mean more effective,' says Dr Lowe.

DO IT YOURSELF

We mentioned do-it-yourself treatments earlier as an alternative to expensive salon procedures. The big question is do they work? Although they promise equal results, few salon professionals would accept that a DIY home treatment could ever be as effective as a salon one. Unless the user is very experienced in using such products, or the instructions are very detailed, the products can be quite hard to use.

TYPES OF TREATMENT

Peels

Home peeling kits are generally designed as an alternative to having a chemical peel in a salon and usually contain a mild acid ingredient. You apply the formula, leave it for a specified period of time, then peel it off. Peeling kits remove the dead skin cells from the top layer of the skin, removing impurities and leaving the skin looking radiant.

Masks

These are products you spread over the face and leave on for several minutes to obtain the best benefit of the ingredients. Once the recommended time has elapsed, you will usually need to peel, rinse or wipe off the mask. Most masks are revitalising and hydrating for the skin, although the result will depend upon the ingredients.

Creams

These are the most traditional anti-ageing formulas, designed to be rubbed into the skin at least once a day to produce the full benefit. Night creams usually have a slightly thicker, richer formula than day creams but both should sink into the skin within a minute of application.

Exfoliants/scrubs

These are products designed to remove dead skin cells from the top layer of the skin. They are usually rubbed roughly over the face and generally contain grains, such as salt, to slough off the dead skin cells and leave skin even and smooth. Scrubs are also good for kick-starting your circulation.

Gels

These tend to be better for slightly younger or oilier skins, as they are not as rich as creams. Again, gels should sink in immediately after application.

Patches

These are placed on specific areas of the skin, to target small areas. They usually need to be left on the skin for some time so that the skin receives the full benefits. Most users tend to apply them in the evening and leave them on overnight. They can be used less frequently than a cream or gel as they have a more intensive result.

A ROUTINE FOR LIFE

Dermatologists recommend adapting your skincare routine every decade:

20 At twenty you should... moisturise with a day cream

30 At thirty you should... also use an eye cream and a night cream

40 At forty you should... use more intensive creams and an anti-ageing pen

50 At fifty you should... find a plumping formula to add volume to your skin

stinging, burning, redness or rashes, rinse off the product and stop using it immediately. All products are carefully tested to ensure they are safe for use, but there is always a rare risk that you may have an adverse reaction to a product. It is also essential to use any product regularly for it to have a visible effect. Guerlain skincare expert Richard Hawkins stresses that you need to use a product every day for a month to get visible, lasting results.

FIGHT THE SIGNS OF AGEING

The general rule with anti-ageing creams – unlike the surgical procedures – is that you can never start too young. In fact, many products are most effective as a preventative measure, as repairing damage that has already been done is a much greater task. Dermatologists recommend adapting your skincare routine at least every decade to keep up with the changing needs of your skin.

In your twenties you should moisturise using a day cream with a good SPF to prevent UV damage. In your thirties you should add an eye cream and a night cream into your routine and ensure your day cream has anti-ageing properties. By your forties, you may need to find a more intensive anti-ageing formula and also purchase an anti-ageing pen which allows you to target specific areas of the face where wrinkles may be more severe, such as round the eyes or pronounced lines between the nose and mouth. In your fifties and sixties, you lose fat in the middle third of your face making it appear gaunt, so lifting is more important than anti-ageing. Find a plumping formula to add volume to your skin and use a moisturiser that will keep skin hydrated for the whole day.

Although genetics, skin type and even face shape have been proven to influence the way people age, it is always good to have a product on hand to help skin remain hydrated and radiant. In this section we test out the most popular creams on the market to see if they live up to their hype and find out what ingredients you should be looking for.

'The general rule with anti-ageing creams – unlike surgical procedures – is that you can never start too young'

DIY kits for things like microdermabrasion (where you use a small sand-jet to blow fine particles on to your skin, removing all the dead cells, opening the pores and, essentially, making your skin taut) can be quite dangerous if not used extremely carefully. While they may deliver results, some of the products can be as expensive as their salon equivalent without the added bonus of having an experienced professional administering them; DIY is undoubtedly not as relaxing an experience. However, most professionals concede that these treatments can be a good alternative to costly salon treatments or a nice treat between professional treatments. The added bonus is that they can be used in the comfort of your own home, so they are more convenient to schedule and less time consuming.

With the BIY products, it is always essential to find the right product for your skin type to deliver the results you want. Make sure you read the label carefully, and check it for the ingredients outlined in the section that follows to assess how effective the product may be. Always follow the instructions and if you have any type of reaction, such as

BUY-IT-YOURSELF TREATMENTS ARE GOOD FOR

☑ regular treatment of a specific problem area

☑ useful as a preventative measure

>>

IF IMITATION IS THE SINCEREST FORM OF FLATTERY, CONSIDER US EXALTE

OVER A DECADE AGO THE SCIENTISTS OF SKINCEUTICALS
developed the original topical vitamin C formula, leading to other
industry-firsts as well as the advent of cosmeceuticals.

In an industry where imitation threatens to replace innovation,
SkinCeuticals continues to raise the bar as the consummate
innovator of anti-aging and photoprotective products. One of
few to develop new technologies backed by true scientific evidence,
SkinCeuticals is the original scientific skincare provider.

SKINCEUTICAL

PREVENTING SUN DAMAGE

Many of us can't help indulging in a little occasional sun-worship, but how much damage is it doing to our skin, and how can we fix it?

LOOK AFTER YOUR MOLES

Skin cancer can develop from or around moles, so it's important to keep track of any changes to your moles and skin. Suspicious moles have ragged or blurred edges, a variety of hues and colours and can bleed or feel itchy. If you notice any unusual new moles or changes to existing ones, you should seek the advice of your GP immediately.

So many of us strive for a perfect tan but rarely appreciate how much the invisible but intense UV (ultraviolet) rays of the sun can damage our skin. Exposure to UV light can accelerate the signs of ageing, making you appear prematurely older, including the appearance of thinner, dry or rough skin, wrinkles and fine red veins. A suntan is, in itself, the result of damage that's been done to the outermost layer of your skin. Sun exposure is a cumulative process so each exposure adds to and builds on the previous exposure. This can, in the worst case scenario, progress into skin cancer. Excessive exposure to UV rays is the most important preventable cause of skin cancer, and preventative measures are easy to take.

PROTECT YOUR SKIN FROM THE SUN

The most effective protection is to start as young as possible and maintain good protection practices. You don't need to hide away indoors; just be smart about your sun exposure and take precautions to keep your skin healthy. For the most complete sun protection, the following methods apply in order of importance:

1 Try to avoid the sun during high-intensity hours from 10 am to 4 pm.

> ' Excessive exposure to UV rays is the most important *preventable* cause of skin cancer '

2 Wear protective clothing, such as long-sleeved shirts, trousers and wide-brimmed hats. A general rule to bear in mind with fabrics is that if you can see light through them, the light can get through to you. Wet clothes can also increase sunlight penetration of fabric. Simply shading your skin from direct sunlight is not adequate, as light can bounce off reflective surfaces like snow, sand or water.

3 Use sunscreen. Sunscreen absorbs, reflects or scatters UV rays. Apply sunscreen at least 20 minutes before going outdoors and reapply every two hours, especially after heavy sweating or after being in water. However, sunscreens don't block out all ultraviolet rays, so other preventative measures also need to be taken. As much as 90% of ultraviolet rays can pass through clouds, so you need to protect your skin any time you're outdoors, even if it doesn't look very sunny outside.

THE ROAD TO RECOVERY

Here is a guide to the most helpful treatments for certain kinds of sun damage. The following information is for guidance use only and does not include developing technologies or new treatments. Always read the label of any product carefully. Avoid products containing mineral oil, also known as petrolatum or paraffin liquidum, as these lure the sun's rays to your skin. You should consult your GP if you are concerned about your skin in any way.

DAMAGE Weakened connective tissues
Look for ingredients to help restore elasticity to skin*:
- collagen
- elastin

DAMAGE Thinner, more translucent-looking skin
You could use a light foundation containing a sun protection factor to avoid further damage. Products that encourage cell renewal and increase metabolism will help strengthen skin tissue.
- Vitamin A Retinol** (acid)
- Vitamin A Retinyl palmitate (oil)

DAMAGE Dry, rough skin
Firstly, drink plenty of water to hydrate your skin. Use products that contain hydrating ingredients:
- jojoba oil
- vitamin E
- hyaluronic acid
- macadamia nut oil
- grape seed oil
- sesame seed oil
- avocado oil
- glycerine, especially compatible with skin when derived from plant resources
Mild exfoliation should also play a part, but be gentle to avoid further damage.

DAMAGE Fine red veins on your cheeks, nose and ears
Also known as broken capillaries, these areas can be sensitive to astringent ingredients, namely toners. To protect them from further damage, you must keep your skin well-hydrated, always wear sun protection and avoid abrasive scrubs.

DAMAGE Uneven pigmentation
Sun damage is often presented in dark patches. Useful treatments include:
- herbal peel
- enzyme peel (biological based)
- acid peel (glycolic, salicylic or lactic acid based)
- chemical (phenol) peels Each type varies in intensity and recovery time. With peel treatments, sunscreen is an aftercare requirement with the exception of some enzyme peels. However, avoiding sun exposure in the first place is key to minimising hyper pigmentation (patches of skin discolouration).

Some products use animal by-products so enquire if you are concerned about ingredient origins.
**Asian skin types are advised to avoid high concentrations of Retinol as it can cause further pigmentation.*

>>

A to Z of key ingredients

So much jargon is used to describe skincare that it can be hard to know where to start. Use our handy guide to the ingredients in your beauty products

GOOD FOR FINE LINES AND WRINKLES
- ☑ acetyl hexapeptide-3 / argireline
- ☑ gaba / gamma-amino-butyric acid
- ☑ furfuryladenine
- ☑ hexapeptide

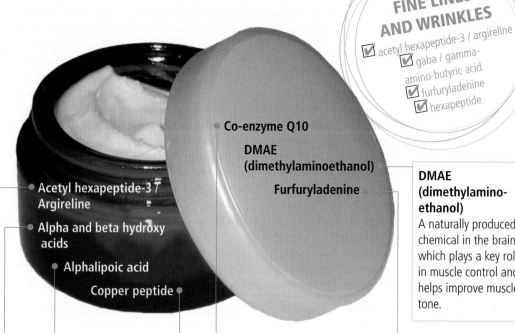

Co-enzyme Q10

DMAE (dimethylaminoethanol)

Furfuryladenine

Acetyl hexapeptide-3 / Argireline

Alpha and beta hydroxy acids

Alphalipoic acid

Copper peptide

Acetyl Hexapeptide-3/ Argireline
This peptide relaxes facial muscles and helps to inhibit muscle contractions, which will reduce wrinkles caused by facial movement. Often referred to as the equivalent of Botox in a jar.

Alpha and beta hydroxy acids
A group of acids which enhance cell renewal. They are usually derived from plants and foods such as fruit and milk. The most common forms are lactic acid, glycolic acid, pyruvic acid, tartaric acid, maleic acid and salicylic acid. In general, they help to promote a smoother, healthier-looking skin.

Alphalipoic acid
A fatty acid that has potent anti-oxidant qualities to fight free radicals and protect and rejuvenate the skin.

Copper peptide
This has recently been discovered to have rejuvenating properties in cell culture studies.

Co-enzyme Q10
Also known as Ubiquinone, this is an anti-oxidant that fights against the damaging effects of the environment.

DMAE (dimethylamino-ethanol)
A naturally produced chemical in the brain which plays a key role in muscle control and helps improve muscle tone.

Furfuryladenine
An ingredient that comes from plants. Tests have shown it can reduce wrinkles, fine lines and other signs of skin ageing without causing skin irritation.

Hexapeptide
This is a non-toxic, non-irritant compound that reduces the excessive stimulation of the facial muscles, relaxing facial tension and reducing the depth of wrinkles.

Gaba / Gamma-Amino-Butyric Acid
GABA is the body's natural muscle relaxing agent, prompting reduced muscle activity, which causes fine lines and wrinkles to disappear.

GOOD FOR HELPING TO PRODUCE COLLAGEN
- ☑ retin A – retinol
- ☑ vitamin A
- ☑ vitamin C

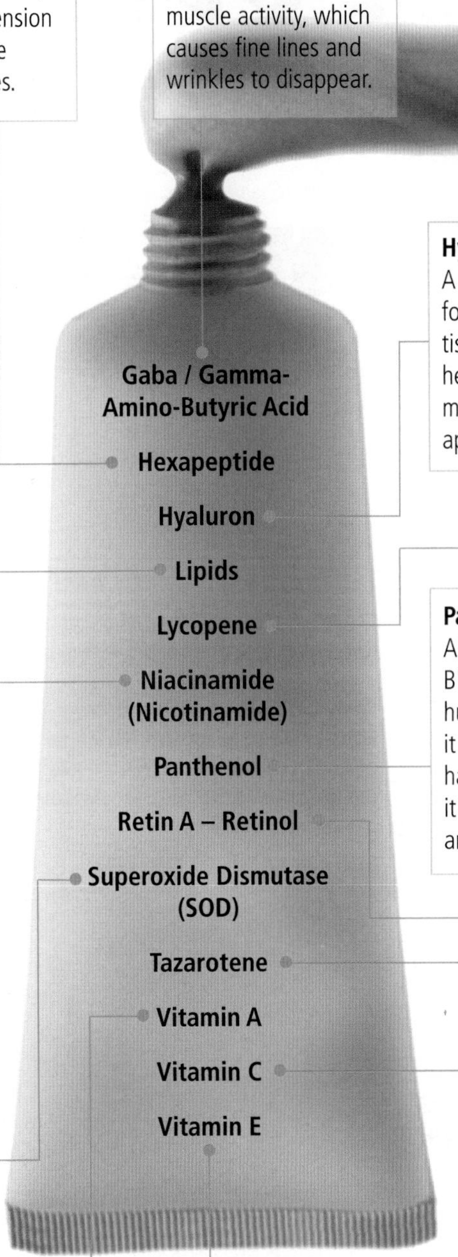

Lipids
These are fats that form a natural part of the skin's barrier. The most important lipids in the skin are ceramides, sterols, sphingolipids and free fatty acids which protect skin and – when combined with humectants or glycerin – make excellent moisturisers.

Hyaluron
A substance usually found in the skin's tissues, hyaluronic acid helps the skin to retain moisture, making it appear plumper.

Lycopene
A proven anti-oxidant that protects the skin from environmental damage, as well as lowering risk of cancer and heart disease. Lycopene is a chemical found in red, yellow and orange-coloured fruits and vegetables.

Panthenol
Also known as vitamin B5, Panthenol is a humectant, meaning it attracts moisture to hair and skin, making it appear smoother and healthier.

Retin A – Retinol
Also known as retinoeic acid, this is a vitamin A-derived acid that speeds cell renewal and collagen production, making skin appear plumper and more youthful.

Niacinamide (Nicotinamide)
Reduces redness and inflammation and can reduce skin ageing that is a result of artificial sunlight. Can also improve the appearance of acne.

Labels on tube:

Gaba / Gamma-Amino-Butyric Acid

Hexapeptide

Hyaluron

Lipids

Lycopene

Niacinamide (Nicotinamide)

Panthenol

Retin A – Retinol

Superoxide Dismutase (SOD)

Tazarotene

Vitamin A

Vitamin C

Vitamin E

Superoxide Dismutase (SOD)
A powerful anti-oxidant that protects the skin against free radical damage. Works as a potent skin-protecting agent. It is available in supplement form from Holland & Barrett stores nationwide, and is soon to become available in skincare formulas.

Vitamin A
A vitamin essential for the maintenance of skin, hair, nails and teeth. Vitamin A also acts as an anti-oxidant and improves skin ageing by increasing collagen formation.

Vitamin E
Also known as tocopherol, this vitamin is an important anti-oxidant which has also been shown to reduce sunburn.

Vitamin C
A vitamin that acts as an anti-oxidant, protecting the skin from UV damage. It also has an important role in the production of collagen.

Tazarotene
Tazarotene has recently been found to reverse some of the effects of skin ageing and is a popular skin rejuvenation cream in the USA. The formula is available in cream form from doctors who give you a prescription.

\>>

on trial

REJUVENATING PRODUCTS ARE HELD UP TO SCRUTINY BY OUR DEDICATED PANEL OF TESTERS

The ratings are based on the testers' experiences of using the products over the course of a month

TREATMENTS

PHILOSOPHY

THE MICRODELIVERY PEEL

CLAIMS: An in-home medical microdermabrasion procedure that rapidly resurfaces the skin as it replenishes it with vitamin C.

IMMEDIATE EFFECT: 'My skin definitely felt softer and smoother.'

EFFECT AFTER ONE MONTH: 'The product was quite abrasive so I could only use it once a week. It left my skin feeling great but I didn't see any improvement in my wrinkles.'

OVERALL COMMENT: 'The texture and smell are lovely – a nice weekly treat even for my sensitive skin.'

£ **£57** (0870 990 8452)

5/10

DIOR

CAPTURE R-MASK SHEET-TYPE INTENSIVE WRINKLE TREATMENT

CLAIMS: A 10-minute wrinkle-correction booster. 10 sheet-type masks, infused with ultra-powerful Capture Serum to boost wrinkle correction. Skin looks instantly smoothed and less lined – radiant with freshness and energy.

IMMEDIATE EFFECT: 'My skin felt soft and smoothed.'

EFFECT AFTER ONE MONTH: 'When used once or twice a week as directed, my skin felt much softer but my wrinkles haven't improved.'

OVERALL COMMENT: 'The mask is quite messy to apply, as it is wet and tends to slide off the face. It stings when you first apply it but this wears off after a few minutes.'

£ **£47.50 FOR 10 MASKS**
(01932 233909)

5/10

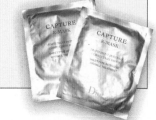

LA PRAIRIE

8/10

SKIN CAVIAR INTENSIVE AMPOULE TREATMENT

CLAIMS: This two-phase treatment system has a formula that diminishes the appearance of fine lines and wrinkles from the moment of application, noticeably smoothing and tightening the skin, while encouraging the reduction of skin discolouration. It slows the ageing process and repairs existing damage.

IMMEDIATE EFFECT: 'Went on nice and smoothly and my skin definitely felt softer.'

EFFECT AFTER ONE MONTH: 'My skin looks and feels plumper with an improved appearance in wrinkles.'

OVERALL COMMENT: 'The product has two tubes that need mixing together but this is easy to do. The liquid is quite thin but easily absorbed. The smell isn't particularly pleasant.'

£ **£335 FOR 6x6ML**
(HOUSE OF FRASER: 0870 160 7270)

SISLEYA

ELIXIR INTENSIVE PROGRAM – RENEWING AND RESTRUCTURING

CLAIMS: Helps to improve vital skin functions and fight the effects of ageing and stress. In the short term, the skin should be hydrated and firmer; in the long-term, skin looks renewed, repaired and younger.

IMMEDIATE EFFECT: 'My skin felt fresher and well-hydrated all day.'

EFFECT AFTER ONE MONTH: 'My skin did feel firmer and the bags under my eyes had noticeably improved. People commented my skin looked less stressed and haggard.'

OVERALL COMMENT: 'You only need to use a few drops each day, so this is very easy to apply. The only drawback is the price.'

£ **£165 FOR 4 X 5ML** (020 7491 2722)

9/10

LANCÔME

6/10

RESURFACE PEEL RESURFACING & SOOTHING SYSTEM

CLAIMS: The first complete home peeling system that combines glycolic acid with a physio peel enhancer to clear away the damaged surface layer and boost the skin's natural renewing process. The AHA (alpha hydroxy acid) lifts dead cells to help fade blemishes and fine lines.

IMMEDIATE EFFECT: 'After my skin sensitivity test, I was able to use the product and found my skin felt tingly and tight after one application.'

EFFECT AFTER ONE MONTH: 'I used it twice a week for four weeks and found the results were cumulative. By week four my skin was much fresher and more radiant.'

OVERALL COMMENT: 'The four-step peeling process was quite complex and time-consuming at first, taking almost half an hour rather than the suggested 10 minutes.'

£ **£95** (AVAILABLE AT DEPARTMENT STORES NATIONWIDE)

DAY CREAMS

FREEZE

24–7 ANTI-WRINKLE CREAM

CLAIMS: Contains GABA (Gamma-Amino-Butyric Acid) which prompts muscle relaxation, causing fine lines and wrinkles to disappear.

IMMEDIATE EFFECT: 'Within 10 minutes of applying the product, the fine lines and wrinkles on my face had significantly decreased. There is a slight tingling sensation when you first apply the product as it gets to work.'

EFFECT AFTER ONE MONTH: 'Although this is only a short-term wrinkle solution, each day after applying the product, my wrinkles were diminished, the pores on my face were refined and reduced and my skin generally felt plumper.'

OVERALL COMMENT: 'Fantastic if used every day. This is highly recommended.'

£65 FOR 30ML (SPACE NK: 020 8740 2085)

10 BEST BUY 10

CRÈME DE LA MER

7/10

MOISTURISING CREAM

CLAIMS: An intensive moisturising cream which delivers vital sustaining hydration. Contains beneficial ingredients from the sea, plus vitamins and nutrients in a unique bio-fermentation process.

IMMEDIATE EFFECT: 'Lasted all day without feeling greasy but the product did take a while to sink into the skin.'

EFFECT AFTER ONE MONTH: 'Skin felt soft, hydrated and more luxuriously cared for.'

OVERALL COMMENT: 'I did not particularly like the consistency – it was quite thick so took time to rub in. I would prefer to use this as a night cream rather than under make-up.'

£145 FOR 60ML (0870 034 2566)

GIVENCHY

NO SURGETICS POWERFUL RECOVERY CARE ANTI-WRINKLE FACE CREAM

CLAIMS: Triple action recovery care: the peel makes skin appear smoother within 2 weeks, the collagen plumps out wrinkles from the inside within 4 weeks and the compress causes facial lines to gradually relax.

IMMEDIATE EFFECT: 'My skin felt much smoother and softer, which lasted for the whole day. My wrinkles seemed temporarily less noticeable.'

EFFECT AFTER ONE MONTH: 'There is a slight improvement in the fine lines and wrinkles on my face.'

OVERALL COMMENT: 'The smell and texture of the cream are fine, although it is greasier than a normal moisturiser – but that is a small price to pay for the pleasing results.'

£43 FOR 50ML (01932 233 909)

8/10

ELEMIS

8/10

CELLULAR RECOVERY SKIN BLISS CAPSULES ANTI-AGEING

CLAIMS: Formulated with anti-oxidants such as moringa oil, rose absolute and lavender to repair the visible signs of ageing and counteract the damaging effects of everyday pollution. This product breaks down the accumulation of harmful toxins that clog up the skin, enabling it to absorb vital nutrients.

IMMEDIATE EFFECT: 'The capsules can be smoothed on really nicely and leave skin feeling soft.'

EFFECT AFTER ONE MONTH: 'My skin looked glowing and particularly felt more radiant when I woke up.'

OVERALL COMMENT: 'You need to apply the contents of one pink rose capsule in the morning and one green lavender capsule at night. I warmed the oil between my palms as directed and massaged in onto my face and neck, it felt very soothing although I think the capsules needed to contain more product.'

£55 FOR 60 CAPSULES
(01278 727830)

NV PERRICONE

10 BEST BUY 10

COSMECEUTICALS NEUROPEPTIDE FACIAL CONTOUR

CLAIMS: This extraordinary neuropeptide-based product is rich in DMAE to create the appearance of a remodelled and recontoured face. It improves the skin's firmness, tone and radiance, reduces redness and minimises the appearance of fine lines and wrinkles.

IMMEDIATE EFFECT: 'My skin felt well moisturised.'

EFFECT AFTER ONE MONTH: 'My skin felt lifted and toned and sagging had visibly reduced. This product was particularly effective on my throat and jawline where there was loose-hanging skin.'

OVERALL COMMENT: 'A fantastic product that lasts for ages – well worth the money. Highly recommended.'

£161 FOR 75ML (WWW.NVPERRICONEMD.CO.UK)

>>

NIGHT CREAMS

VITA LIBERATA

7/10

REST & REJUVENATE COLLAGEN NIGHT CREAM

CLAIMS: Creates visibly softer, smoother and rejuvenated skin. With hyaluron for plump youthful skin, ginkgo biloba for anti-oxidant support, black willow for cell renewal, and yam for fresh blood supply.

IMMEDIATE EFFECT: 'My skin felt really soft.'

EFFECT AFTER ONE MONTH: 'There were no major changes but my skin did feel smooth and silky.'

OVERALL COMMENT: 'I liked the fact the product used natural extracts, although the smell was a bit off-putting. The texture was just right so the cream rubbed in easily.'

£32.50 FOR 50ML (0289 334 4411)

L'OREAL

REVITALIFT NIGHT ANTI-WRINKLE & FIRMING CREAM

CLAIMS: Revitalift Night uses nanosomes of Pro-Retinol A and Dermolastyl R to reduce the appearance of wrinkles, firm up and revitalise the skin. Within 4 weeks the number of wrinkles will be reduced and each morning your features will be rested, making your skin fresher, softer and visibly younger.

IMMEDIATE EFFECT: 'Nice to apply but no instant effects.'

EFFECT AFTER ONE MONTH: 'After using every night for a month, I found my skin did feel fresher and brighter each morning but the wrinkles were still there!'

OVERALL COMMENT: 'Nice but didn't make a dent in the wrinkles!'

£12.99 FOR 50ML (0800 072 6699)

6/10

RoC

5/10

RETIN-OX CORREXION NIGHT

CLAIMS: Contains a combination of Retinol and CollagenOx to reduce expression lines on the surface of the skin and correct the appearance of even the deepest wrinkles during the night.

IMMEDIATE EFFECT: 'There is an immediate tightening effect, with slight tingling and redness.'

EFFECT AFTER ONE MONTH: 'My skin feels slightly plumped out but my wrinkles have not improved.'

OVERALL COMMENT: 'Really lovely fragrance. A small amount spreads generously and smoothly over the face but it is not very effective.'

£24.95 FOR 30ML (AVAILABLE FROM BOOTS)

YSL

LISSE EXPERT EYE AND LIP ANTI-WRINKLE CONCENTRATE – ANTI-AGE

CLAIMS: Fights against the formation of wrinkles on the most vulnerable areas of the face. The Gluco-Peptide complex rebuilds a dense network of elastic fibres to smooth away wrinkles and improve the tone and radiance of the eye and lip contour.

IMMEDIATE EFFECT: 'No immediate results.'

EFFECT AFTER ONE MONTH: 'The applicator did not even contain enough product for 2 weeks usage, so I did not see any results.'

OVERALL COMMENT: 'I used the product day and night as directed but found it did not last long and was very difficult to get out of the tube. The texture and smell were fine.'

£26 FOR 7.5ML (01444 255 700)

3/10

LIP TREATMENTS

SKIN DOCTORS

COSMECEUTICALS PERFECT POUT

CLAIMS: This incredible lip plumping serum can help make lips appear to swell and expand to a fuller pout. You will see the results in 60 seconds or less, and the results can last for hours.

IMMEDIATE EFFECT: 'There was an almost uncomfortable tingling sensation when I first applied the product which wore off after 5 minutes. My lips looked instantly plumper and fuller, which lasted for several hours.'

EFFECT AFTER ONE MONTH: 'The results are only temporary and not cumulative, so you would have to apply the product regularly over the course of a day to maintain the results.'

OVERALL COMMENT: 'The results were instant and pleasing, although it did not last very long and will not make a long-term difference to my lips.'

6/10

£19.95 FOR 8ML (0845 408 1445)

EYE TREATMENTS

SPA SCIENCES

MATRIXYL 3000 EYE PATCH THERAPY

CLAIMS: Helps reduce appearance of fine lines and crow's feet while simultaneously hydrating the eyes. The double peptide complex stimulates hyaluronic acid in the skin to retain moisture, keeping skin plumped and smoothed. Contains hydrolysed collagen to make skin appear softer and firmer.
IMMEDIATE EFFECT: 'I felt relaxed and well-rested.'
EFFECT AFTER ONE MONTH: 'My eyes did feel plumped, smooth and hydrated.'
OVERALL COMMENT: 'The patches are in a handy half-moon shape so they are easy to apply. It was nice to relax and leave the patch on for 30-40 minutes if I was in for the evening, though not ideal if I was going out.'

£ **£9.99 FOR 32 PATCHES** (AVAILABLE FROM BOOTS)

7/10

SKIN DOCTORS

COSMECEUTICALS EYETUCK

CLAIMS: Eyetuck will give your under eyes a smoother, tighter-looking appearance in a matter of weeks, while using natural skin conditioners such as apricot oil and shea butter to help care for and protect this delicate area.
IMMEDIATE EFFECT: 'There was no effect after one application. I already use an eye cream though, so this may be why I didn't see instant results.'
EFFECT AFTER ONE MONTH: 'There was a definite improvement to the wrinkles around my eyes and my under-eye bags within two weeks.'
OVERALL COMMENT: 'The product was nice and light to use and a little goes a long way. The packaging was ideal, with a neat pump to dispense just the right amount of product. I will certainly continue to use it.'

£ **£32.95**
FOR 15ML
(0845 408 1445)

8/10

NECK CREAMS

GATINEAU

DEFILIFT THROAT AND DECOLLETE CREAM

CLAIMS: Smoothes wrinkles on the throat and improves the appearance of the throat and decollete (lower neck) by lifting and firming thin, fragile skin and nourishing with camelia oil, allantoin and vitamins A, E and F.
IMMEDIATE EFFECT: 'The skin on my throat did feel slightly tighter after one use.'
EFFECT AFTER ONE MONTH: 'My skin is tauter and smoother, with fewer tell-tale wrinkles.'
OVERALL COMMENT: 'This product can be used morning and evening, as it was non-greasy and didn't leave a build-up of product on my skin.'

£ **£45 FOR 50ML** (0800 731 5805)

7/10

CELLULITE TREATMENTS

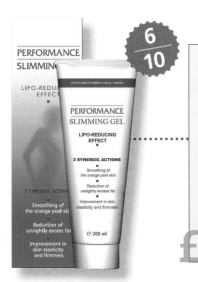

6/10

ARKOPHARMA

PERFORMANCE SLIMMING GEL WITH LIPO-REDUCING EFFECT

CLAIMS: Smoothes orange peel skin, reduces unsightly excess fat and improves skin elasticity and firmness.
IMMEDIATE EFFECT: 'My skin did tingle after applying the product so it felt like it was working.'
EFFECT AFTER ONE MONTH: 'My skin does appear a bit tighter and smoother.'
OVERALL COMMENT: 'I found it hard to apply the product twice a day as it took a while to sink in to my skin. I found it worked better if I spent some time massaging it in.'

£ **£16.95 FOR 200ML** (020 8763 1414)

ESTÉE LAUDER

9/10

BODY PERFORMANCE SLIM ANTI-CELLULITE VISIBLE CONTOURING SERUM

CLAIMS: A triple-action serum that fights stubborn cellulite. Powerful ingredients such as St Paulswort, Forskolin, Guarana and Chinese Black Tea diminish the appearance of cellulite and prevent it from resurfacing.
IMMEDIATE EFFECT: 'There was a cool, tingling effect after the first application and my legs felt tight for several hours.'
EFFECT AFTER ONE MONTH: 'I have lost almost a centimetre from around my thighs and they appear slightly less dimpled.'
OVERALL COMMENT: 'I had to apply this product twice a day to get optimum results, so a bottle does not last that long but I was pleased with the results.'

£ **£28 FOR 200ML** (0870 034 2566)

It's all about looking good and feeling great

The better we look, the better we feel. And the answer to looking rejuvenated, revitalised and refreshed couldn't be easier... quicker... or safer.

RESTYLANE is the UK's leading aesthetic treatment of its kind. And it's easy to see why.

In an instant, it hydrates the skin and adds definition – enhancing looks in a subtle and natural way.

It's long lasting too – from around six months to a year. But it's not permanent, which means you stay in control of the way you look.

And that is the real beauty of RESTYLANE.

Restylane

NATURAL BEAUTY MADE IN SWEDEN

For further information about RESTYLANE, and details of your local RESTYLANE practitioner, please call FREEPHONE 0800 015 5548

RENEW   REFRESH   REJUVENATE   REVITALISE   REVIVE   REPLENISH

www.restylane.co.uk

3

non-invasive treatments

FACE AND BODY

If your moisturiser is no longer disguising your deepening wrinkles and you don't feel ready to go under the surgeon's knife, then non-invasive surgical procedures offer a great alternative. With fewer risks and far less healing time than invasive surgery, non-invasive treatments are becoming more and more popular every day. The range of available procedures is outlined in this section to help you decide which treatment is right for you.

introduction to

non -

A recent survey in the *Economist* revealed there has been a 400% increase in cosmetic surgery procedures over the last 5 years, and 80% of that rise is accounted for by non-surgical treatments

invasive

TECHNIQUES & SALON TREATMENTS

WHETHER YOU WANT more youthful skin, less dimply thighs or perkier breasts, there is a non-invasive alternative to surgery that is capable of achieving great results.

As we age, our bad habits, hormonal problems, years of sun exposure, poor diet, sluggish circulation and stress all start to take their toll on our appearance and rob our skin of vital nutrients. Simultaneously, fat, muscle and bone all decrease as we get older, leading to thinning skin, flattening of the face, hollowing of the eyes and the formation of wrinkles. What nature has taken out, we need to put back in, and sometimes no amount of diet and exercise will be enough.

The following sections outline the non-invasive cosmetic means of reintroducing nutrients to the skin to spur on the body's production of collagen and plump up any hollowed out features. From injectables to peels, lasers and light therapy, there are a host of ways to rejuvenate the face

and body to get back your youthful radiance – and these methods are growing in popularity. A recent survey in the *Economist* revealed there has been a 400% increase in cosmetic surgery procedures over the last 5 years, and 80% of that rise is accounted for by non-surgical treatments. Non-invasive treatments are becoming so commonplace that fitting fillers into your lunch hour or attending a Botox party with your friends is now as quick and easy as an appointment with your hairdresser.

Before undertaking any procedure, however, be sure to have a thorough consultation with the practitioner. Prices will vary according to the size of the area to be treated, so use our guide as a good starting point for how much money will be involved. On top of this, always make sure your practitioner has had the appropriate training to ensure safety, as well as a fantastic visible result. Read on and prepare for a new, younger you...

NATURAL WAYS

Non-invasive cosmetic procedures include invigorating exfoliating face peels and line smoothing injections, as well as laser and light procedures that involve the transmission of radiowaves deep into the skin, promoting the production of new collagen within your own body.

THE FACE

We all know that, as the years pass, there are more flaws to attend to in the mirror, with skincare rituals that gradually increase in length. In this section we reveal the ways to improve the appearance of fine lines and wrinkles and make your face appear more youthful. We look at how to remove the small veins that appear under the surface of the skin, and ways to restore firmness to skin that has lost its laxity, just to make your morning mirror session that bit easier...

line smoothing

Facial wrinkles and deep-set lines are a sure sign of ageing, but there are some non-invasive cosmetic procedures available that will smooth your worry lines away swiftly and easily

AUTOLOGOUS CELL THERAPY (ISOLAGEN)

What is it?
As we age, our body gets worse at producing its own collagen (the substance that gives our skin its elasticity) so the Isolagen process gives nature a helping hand. A small sample of cells is taken from your own body, then cultivated and injected back into your skin to encourage the natural production of collagen to smooth wrinkles and repair scars. No foreign substances are used; just cells derived from your own body.

GOOD FOR?
- ✓ décolleté creases
- ✓ fine lines and wrinkles
- ✓ crow's feet
- ✓ lines from the nose to the mouth (nasolabial creases)
- ✓ plumping up hands
- ✓ acne scars

How it's done
A local anaesthetic is given and a small incision is made behind the ear, where a 4mm sample of skin is removed (this is a biopsy). This sample is then sent to a laboratory where the fibroblasts (collagen-producing cells) are grown. After 8-10 weeks, the new cells are injected back into the body with a fine needle with only minimal discomfort. A session lasts between 30-45 minutes, and a course of two treatments is advised, with a 30-45 day interval between the two visits.

Time to heal
The skin sample taken is very small to minimise pain, and the skin in this area should heal quickly. There may be light bruising immediately after the injections but this will reduce overnight. The reddening and soreness fade after one day.

How long will the effects last?
The results are subtle and gradual, with most patients starting to see results 3-6 months post-treatment. The increased fibroblast cells in your skin will continue to stimulate collagen and elastin production – elastin is similar to collagen – for 12-18 months, so results are long lasting. Patients are recommended to have 'top-up' treatments once a year to keep the skin refreshed.

Is it safe?
Autologous cell therapy is a recognised medical procedure currently in the process of being regulated by the Healthcare Commission in England and Wales. There is no allergy risk, as the process uses your own cells. To date, over 7,500 Isolagen treatments have been administered with no serious adverse reactions.

What should I ask?
Check your Isolagen practitioner has undertaken the compulsory training programme, accredited by The Royal College of Surgeons.

Is it right for me?
Although most clients are in their late thirties or forties, some people in their late twenties often have a skin sample removed and sent to the laboratory ready to create cells. These youthful collagen-producing cells are then stored, ready for when the patient wants the full treatment in a later period in life.

Contraindications
This procedure should be avoided by pregnant women, as well as people with keloid scarring and auto-immune system diseases.

BEFORE

The cheeks are rejuvenated

AFTER

ISOLAGEN

£ **PRICE**
From £2,950 for a skin sample and course of two injections

'Patients observe an improvement in skin quality, skin texture and elasticity. The skin looks healthier… Also, because the cells are much healthier and younger, the skin has a glow'

Susan Segall Isolagen practitioner for Rejuvenate UK

BOTOX

What is it?
Botox is a wrinkle smoother made from Botulinum toxin. Essentially, it is a muscle relaxant that blocks the production of acetylcholine, the chemical that encourages muscle contraction. Injecting Botox into muscles in the skin paralyses them temporarily, so wrinkles appear smoother.

\>\>

>> BOTOX

How it's done

Botox is injected in highly diluted doses into specific facial muscles using a small, fine needle. This causes the muscle to become temporarily paralysed, which softens lines and contours. Several injections are usually needed at specific sites, depending on the area being treated. Treatment takes 10-15 minutes and is often referred to as a lunchtime procedure.

Time to heal

Botox doesn't require any healing time – you can resume your normal activities immediately.

How long will the effects last?

Botox usually takes effect 1-3 days after the injections, with maximum effect 1-2 weeks later. The effects last for about 3-4 months.

Is it safe?

In less than 1% of people it can cause weakness in muscles near the injection site, resulting in a slight temporary drooping of the eyelid or eyebrow, known as ptosis. A very rare side effect is frozen face syndrome, where the patient can no longer create a full range of facial expressions, but this can be avoided by having fewer injections in fewer sites. If the wrong muscle were paralysed, it would only be temporary. Botox is now used so widely – and safely – that it has been approved by medical authorities in over 70 countries.

What should I ask?

You should ask about recently announced plans that would require clinics offering Botox to register with the Healthcare Commission in 2006.

Is it right for me?

Candidates tend to be in their thirties.

Contraindications

It should be avoided by pregnant or breast-feeding women, and those taking certain muscle relaxants.

GOOD FOR?
- ☑ crow's feet
- ☑ forehead lines
- ☑ neck muscles
- ☑ the corners of the mouth
- ☑ upper lip lines
- ☑ noticeably deep lines in the face

DID YOU KNOW?

● 100,000 Botox injections are given in the UK annually

● Botox is the most popular cosmetic procedure in the UK

● Botox parties have become a recent craze, with patients sipping champagne whilst being treated. However, some experts have warned of safety concerns over mixing Botox with alcohol

£ PRICE
From £175-£300 per area treated

>> BOTOX CASE STUDY

Patient: Gail, 42, PA in a law firm
Treatment type: Line smoothing
Brand: Botox
Area of treatment: Forehead

Q Why did you choose this particular treatment?
A Some of my friends tried Botox and I was amazed at the results. The frown lines on my forehead had been bothering me for some time and this seemed like a safe and simple way to improve them.

Q Where did you get treatment and who administered it?
A I went to a Transform medical clinic where a qualified doctor administered the Botox. I had an introductory session a week or so before the procedure so that I could ask questions about the treatment – that was invaluable in putting my mind at rest.

Q How long did it take?
A The whole procedure only lasted 15 minutes – I was so pleased I didn't need to take any time off.

Q How did you feel during and after treatment? How did you look immediately afterwards?
A I was slightly nervous beforehand but I needn't have been – it was all over so quickly! The injections were uncomfortable but not painful, like having a jab at the doctors, and my face only felt slightly sore for around a day. I could start to see the difference immediately, but it wasn't until a couple of days later that other people commented on it.

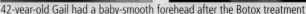

BEFORE / AFTER

42-year-old Gail had a baby-smooth forehead after the Botox treatment

Q Did you suffer any negative side effects?
A None at all. I found the whole process pretty quick and painless.

Q Were you immediately satisfied, or did it take time to see the full benefits?
A It only took a day or two for the full benefits to show – I'm thrilled with the results.

Q What impact has the treatment had on your life?
A I am so much more confident – it's given me a new lease of life.

Q Do you have any advice for someone considering Botox?
I think it's a very simple way of improving your appearance without going through the pain and expense of surgery.

skin freshening

Although the idea of applying a chemical solution to your skin may seem daunting, a chemical peel is not an 'acid face-mask' – it's an effective method of exfoliation which helps you replace the outer layers of wrinkled, blemished skin with fresh, younger-looking layers

CHEMICAL PEELS

What is it?

A chemical solution is applied to the skin and left on for a specified period of time to carefully remove the outer layers of aged or damaged skin. There are three different types of peel: light (glycolic or salicylic acid), medium (trichloroacetic (TCA) acid) and deep (phenol acid), with the deeper peels being more uncomfortable but giving more dramatic results.

How it's done

● The glycolic acid peel is the mildest exfoliating peel available, removing dead cells from the top layer of skin. This treatment can be performed in 10-15 minutes and is only as painful as a vigorous exfoliator. This is the best peel for boosting the skin's vibrancy.
● The TCA peel uses trichloroacetic acids to gently remove the outer layers of the skin. Because it penetrates the middle skin layer, this peel actually restores the lower collagen and elastin layers of the skin and will cause mild discomfort. It is a 15-minute procedure and is the best peel for removing fine lines.
● A phenol peel is the strongest type of chemical peel, using carbolic acid for deep exfoliation of the face, best for treating things like sun damage and scarring. The peel is rather painful, with skin feeling hot and sore, so it is important to let your practitioner know if you feel you are in too much discomfort. Also called Xeodern, this kind of peel takes at least two hours.

During treatment the skin will feel hot, so after the procedure there will be a short cooling down period when cold swabs will be applied to the skin. Sedation levels will depend on the depth of the peel you're having.

Time to heal

Glycolic acid peels are not aggressive. The skin may be slightly red at first, but will heal fully within a couple of days. TCA peels create moderate discomfort and swelling for about a week, and minimal scabbing which will last for a few days. The recovery time for a phenol peel is around 1-3 weeks and skin will be very red after the procedure. Patients are generally left with a feeling of sunburn or windburn. Factor 30 sunblock must be worn for at least six months following treatment to protect the skin, and you should avoid extremes of hot and cold for a few days after treatment.

How long will the effects last?

Superficial peels need to be repeated weekly for 4-6 weeks to obtain a good result, and then maintained monthly. Medium peels will need maintaining every 6-12 months. With deep peels, it may be around 3-4 months before you see the full benefits, but after the initial shedding of the skin layers, your skin will look fresher with reduced wrinkles and more even skin tone, with results lasting up to 10 years.

Is it safe?

Chemical peels are not currently regulated by the Healthcare Commission in England and Wales.

BEFORE

The skin is much smoother

AFTER

LUCY GLANCEY

GOOD FOR?

- ☑ age spots
- ☑ sun-damaged skin
- ☑ imperfections caused by acne
- ☑ uneven pigmentation
- ☑ fine lines and wrinkles
- ☑ boosting skin's vibrancy
- ☑ scarring

TYPES OF PEEL

Light
For mild skin damage – immediate recovery

Medium
For moderate skin damage, lines and pigmentation – 7 days' recovery time

Deep
For severe sun damage, wrinkles, lines and pigmentation – 3 weeks' recovery time

'To many people, the very word peeling conjures up horror – the idea of going tomato red and chilli-pepper sore and then peeling like a snake over several days or weeks. However, this is one of the simplest, yet most effective, anti-ageing and anti-malignant skin treatments that there is'

Dr Mark Palmer, cosmetic physician

The MediSpa Clinic

The UK's 1st Medical Day Spa based in Cheshire

Your ultimate experience under one roof!

Surgical

Twilight, also known as 'Conscious Sedation'. A smaller dose of anaesthetic medication which relaxes the patient while the surgical area is numbed using a local anaesthetic. This does not actually put you to sleep during the procedure and you should not recall feeling any discomfort during the surgery. Other surgical procedures covered include Breast Enlargement, Breast Reduction, Breast Uplift, Liposuction, Facial Surgery, Tummy Tucks (Abdominoplasty), Ear Correction, Cheek and Chin Implants, Removal of Moles and Cysts, and Pectoral Implants.

Non-Surgical

Our Medispa Counsellors will go through treatment options available to you, before handing you over to our Medical Director Dr Roy Saleh, whose dedication, years of experience and attention to detail has developed international acclaim, assuring that our non surgical, enhancement treatments are delivered to the safest and highest standards.

Dr Roy Saleh is one of the most renowned surgeons in England to offer rejuvenation, facial and body enhancement, performing over 15000 **Botox**®, 2000 **Fillers**, 1000 **Red Vein** treatments plus over 1000 **Skin Peels** and 150 **Mid Face Lipo Lifts**® per year.

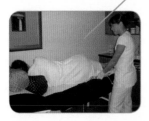

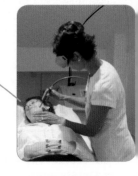

Colonic / Lifestyle Treatments

At the MediSpa Clinic we don't just offer you the chance to enhance your appearance; we also offer the opportunity to better your health. As a well-known cancer and other serious illness preventative, Colonic Irrigation relieves the body from toxins and harmful bacteria.

Beauty

We cover top-to-toe treatments. Either as a small treatment or as part of a pampering package, Facials, Manicures and Pedicures can make a woman feel cherished and perfect a look for that special occasion.

Laser

Laser can offer a simple and long lasting alternative to hair removal, as well as rejuvenating the skin, removing thread veins and acne scars and works on all skin types. The treatment is carried out by specially trained Laser practitioners.

London Road, Adlington, SK10 4DU

www.themedispaclinic.com   Tel: **0845 605 6005**   Fax: **01625 827981**

>> CHEMICAL PEELS

The depth of the chemical peel relates directly to the pain you will experience and the number of possible side effects you could encounter. You must be prepared for some skin redness and discomfort, and there is a small risk of infection, scarring or hyperpigmentation (where treated areas of the face turn a whitish colour). However, no matter how deep the peel, your skin will re-grow and should heal fully.

What should I ask?

Always have a thorough consultation with your practitioner to ensure you're getting the right type of peel for your skin type, and for your particular skin problem.

Is it right for me?

The older you are, the more damage there will be to treat, so the stronger the peel programme will be required to gain visible results. Clients are in their teens and twenties for acne and spots, and thirties and upwards for skin maintenance.

Contraindications

Peels should be avoided by dark skin types and anyone on steroids or Roaccutane (used for acne).

£

PRICE
From £60 per treatment for mild glycolic peels, to over £500 for a course of four TCA peels and over £2,000 for the deeper peels

youthful fillers

Dermal fillers are materials injected into the skin in areas where it needs to be plumped up and made to look firmer. Different fillers have different degrees of permanence, with some having a temporary lifespan of only six months while others can last a lifetime

TEMPORARY FILLERS

As the skin ages, it gradually loses some of its collagen and fat, leaving it looking wrinkled and saggy. The use of dermal fillers to help plump out lines and wrinkles has seen tremendous growth recently in the UK, with more people than ever having this treatment as a cheap and effective alternative to surgery. Temporary fillers tend to last between six months and two years, and their shorter lifespan is part of their appeal, letting you see if you like the effects before progressing to a more permanent solution.

What is it?

Temporary dermal fillers are made of various kinds of natural (human or bovine) and man-made or synthetic materials that have been developed for injection into the skin. Depending on the type of filler used and the area treated, the general effect will be a plumping out of the skin and a more youthful, firmer look.

How it's done

All substances are injected using a fine needle inserted at several points along the edge of the treatment site. For very small areas – such as nasolabial creases between the nose and mouth – only one injection may be necessary. Each product is injected into a different layer of the skin, and different consistencies are used for different depths of wrinkles. Generally speaking, the more viscous the filler, the deeper it is injected. Depending on the area treated and which filler is used, treatment times can vary from around 30 minutes to an hour. You may feel some minor stinging or burning as the injections are administered.

Time to heal

There may be some swelling or bruising initially, but this will heal quickly after a day or two.

How long will the effects last?

Results usually last between six months and two years, depending on which product is injected and how much is used. To maintain results, the injection must be repeated at regular intervals.

GOOD FOR?
- ☑ crow's feet
- ☑ forehead wrinkles
- ☑ lines from the nose to the corners of the mouth and round the lips
- ☑ smile lines on the cheeks
- ☑ chin and cheek contours
- ☑ hand wrinkles

'Most injectable fillers only treat wrinkles, lines and folds but Restylane SubQ looks at the overall face shape and can help clients to achieve the most desirable 'triangle' shape, with youthful high cheekbones'

Dr Rajiv Grover consultant plastic surgeon for NW London Regional Centre for Plastic Surgery

>>

>> TEMPORARY FILLERS

Every person's skin will react differently and gradually absorb the fillers at a different rate. As such you may need to have repeat injections after six months, or you could be lucky and be able to wait two years between treatments.

Is it safe?
Due to the temporary nature of these fillers, they will soon be dispersed into the body. Most are made from natural substances so will not cause adverse reactions. Rare allergic reactions can occur after some treatments, however, so an allergy skin test must be performed the month before a bovine collagen procedure, as 2% of people have an allergic reaction to this substance. Dermal fillers are not currently regulated by the Healthcare Commission in England and Wales,

but clinics offering fillers are required to register with the Healthcare Commission in 2006.

What should I ask?
Make sure you have a practitioner who is certified for the specific filler and the area they are treating.

Is it right for me?
Clients tend to be in their thirties for lips and contours, and their forties for lines and wrinkles.

Contraindications
Pregnancy or allergic reaction to a particular filler. Do not use bovine collagen if you have suffered from autoimmune system deficiencies, rheumatoid arthritis, psoriatic arthritis, systemic or discoid lupus erythematosus or polymyositis.

£ PRICE
From £150-£750 depending on the type of filler used and the number of syringes

>> TEMPORARY FILLERS CASE STUDY

Patient: Lorna, 36, media relations consultant
Type of treatment: Temporary filler
Brand: Restylane and Restylane SubQ
Area of treatment: Nose to mouth lines (nasolabial creases), frown lines on forehead and cheeks

BEFORE / AFTER

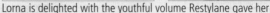
Q-MED UK RESTYLANE

Q Why did you decide to have this treatment?
A I work as a media relations consultant, so looking good is very much part of my job. By last year, however, I found that the long hours and travelling were starting to take their toll on my appearance. I wasn't looking as energetic as my younger colleagues, despite my best efforts at the gym and using a variety of expensive beauty products.

Q Why did you choose Restylane?
A I researched all the options thoroughly and liked the fact that Restylane is derived from a substance that naturally occurs in our bodies. Restylane SubQ is long lasting and biodegrades slowly over about 12 months. This appeals to me, as I don't like the idea of unnatural invasive procedures.

Q Where did you go for treatment and who administered it?
A I went to Rajiv Grover's practice on Harley Street in London.

Q How long did your treatment take?
A It was very fast – the whole things was over and done with in less than an hour.

Q How did you feel during and after treatment, and how did you look immediately afterwards?
A The injections stung a little but I wasn't in a lot of pain and I didn't need to take any time off to heal. I could see the results straight away, and was very pleased with them.

Q Did you suffer any negative side effects?
A None at all.

Q Were you immediately satisfied, or did it take time to see the full benefits?
A Yes, the Restylane treatment instantly softened the deep lines between my nose and mouth and smoothed the frown lines at the top of my nose. I was so pleased with the results that I recently had new Restylane SubQ to give my cheeks back their youthful volume.

Q What impact has the treatment had on your life?
A I'm absolutely delighted with

Lorna is delighted with the youthful volume Restylane gave her

the look. It has given my face more shape and definition and provided me with a much needed confidence boost.

Q Do you have any advice for someone considering this treatment?
A This is a great alternative to invasive procedures particularly if, like me, you're too busy to take time off work to heal. I am more than happy to use Restylane to put off the day when I might have to consider going under the knife.

NON-INVASIVE

SEMI-PERMANENT / PERMANENT FILLERS

Temporary fillers can be useful to try, but you may want a more permanent solution at a later date. Semi-permanent fillers still offer an element of choice, while permanent fillers give you the satisfaction of knowing you won't need a repeat treatment. Modern more permanent fillers can be made from all kinds of different materials, ranging from your own fat cells to beads, gels and other materials that can be injected into wrinkles to plump them out.

What is it?
● The Autologous fat transplant procedure (Lipotransfer) involves taking fat from one part of your body (such as the bottom, hips, inner thighs, or abdomen), cleaning and filtering it, then injecting it back into another part of your body, such as the face. This is the most natural of all the facial fillers as it uses your body's own cells. Harvested fat can also be frozen and stored if touch-ups are needed in the future.
● Polymethylmethacrylate (PMMA, Artecoll, Artefill) is made from a mixture of tiny plastic (methylmethacrylate) beads and bovine collagen. The mixture is injected underneath the skin, and the plastic beads become encapsulated in scar tissue. The collagen holds the plastic beads in place, which can then last for months or years after the collagen has dispersed.
● PTFE implants (Gore-Tex, Gore SAM, SoftForm) use PTFE (polytetrafluoroethylene), which is made from synthetic polymers such as carbon. They are softer than silicone implants.

Human blood vessels flow directly into the material, so it's very well tolerated by the body.
● Polyacrylamide (Aquamid) implants are 97% water and are composed of a highly polymerised polyacrylamide gel – silicone gel – similar to the material used in soft contact lenses.

How it's done
For the Autologous fat transplant, fat is withdrawn using a liposuction syringe attached to a suction device. Once the fat has been prepared, it is then injected with great care into the recipient site using a needle. For the other treatments, the practitioner either injects the implants (Polymethylmethacrylate and Polyacrylamide) or surgically inserts them beneath the skin (PTFE implants). Sedation levels vary depending on the procedure. With all procedures, there will be slight discomfort as the materials are inserted, but the injections are very small to ensure there is only minimal discomfort and no scarring.

Time to heal
Expect swelling or bruising for anything from several days to several weeks, depending on the type of procedure and size of the area being filled. Patients are advised to stay indoors, out of the sun, until the redness and bruising subsides.

How long will the effects last?
The results can last from several years to forever, effectively, depending on how much filler is used and how deeply it is injected. However, repeat injections may be necessary.

GOOD FOR?
☑ filling in sunken cheeks
☑ smoothing laughter lines around the eyes
☑ filling out deep lines between the nose and mouth
☑ minimising forehead wrinkles
☑ enhancing the lips
☑ smoothing skin depressions or indentations

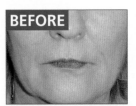
BEFORE

Lips have been subtly filled

AFTER

ANGELICA KAVOUNI

TYPES OF FILLER

HYALURONIC ACID-BASED PRODUCT (RESTYLANE OR PERLANE)
Hyaluronic acid is a substance naturally found in the body which helps the skin to retain moisture better.

COLLAGEN
Commonly used in fillers, it is naturally found in the skin, keeping it pliant and toned. Our collagen production decreases as we age.

BOVINE COLLAGEN
Made of sterile, purified collagen from cow skin, rather than human skin.

EVOLENCE
A new product which also uses collagen, although, instead of human or bovine variations, it is made from organic collagen, purified and transformed to produce a synthetic compound.

CALCIUM HYDROXYLAPATITE
A synthetic filler that has been safely used in dental procedures to build up bone for reconstruction.

POLYLACTIC ACID
Also a synthetic filler that is designed as a sculpting agent rather than just a wrinkle filler, so it is able to treat larger areas with longer-lasting results.

>>

>> SEMI PERMANENT / PERMANENT FILLERS

Is it safe?

The Autologous fat transplant has no risk of an allergic reaction as it uses your own fat. With all treatments, however, lumps and bumps are possible. Be prepared for a lot of swelling if you have your lips done. Permanent fillers should not cause tissue reactions and should be readily removable should the need arise. Possible side effects include scarring at the incision points, infection, numbness or nerve damage, minor skin discolouration and potential hardness over the injected area. Semi-permanent fillers have the dual advantage of being very long lasting but more easily removable, should the desire arise.

What should I ask?

Check which of the semi-permanent fillers is best suited to your skin, whether you will need any allergy tests or more than one treatment.

Is it right for me?

Clients receiving these more permanent fillers tend to be in their forties and fifties.

Contraindications

Hypersensitivity or allergy to the active ingredient, any disease affecting the immune system, susceptibility to keloids, steroid treatment, pregnancy or breast-feeding.

£ PRICE
From £800-£1,500, depending on how many areas are treated

healing rays

There are many non-invasive healing procedures involving lights and lasers that will help your skin repair itself and become firm and supple

FRAXEL LASER

What is it?

The Fraxel laser fires a laser beam which produces tiny, microscopic columns in the skin known as microthermal treatment zones. Essentially, the laser causes the skin to repair itself by rebuilding collagen. Rather than the whole area being treated at once, the treated areas are separated by areas of unaffected, healthy tissue, because they help to promote faster healing. The Fraxel laser offers the benefits of traditional laser resurfacing without the uncomfortable side effects.

How it's done

A local anaesthetic is applied one hour before treatment. A blue tint is then applied to the skin, which darkens the skin surface and shows up the tiny folds that need treatment. The laser handpiece then acts only on the folds that have been darkened with the blue dye. The laser handpiece uses an optical tracking system (IOTS) to ensure that the laser only targets the portions of your skin that require attention. The Fraxel laser treatment may sound like a scary prospect, but it only causes

GOOD FOR?
☑ lines and wrinkles
☑ pigmentation and age spots
☑ tattoo removal
☑ acne scarring
☑ skin that has lost its firmness
☑ sun-damaged skin
☑ chest and neck
☑ lines and wrinkles on the back of the hand

minimal discomfort, and just feels like your skin is being warmed. The treatment only takes around 40-45 minutes to complete.

Time to heal

Immediate effects include slight puffiness, swelling and a mild sunburn sensation that will last for around an hour. Skin will be slightly pink for roughly 48 hours and may be slightly swollen and red for up to 5-7 days. The results will be visible within a week.

How long will the effects last for?

After your first treatment, skin will gradually become softer, smoother and fresher. Fine lines around the eyes, uneven colouring and age spots will fade noticeably. Four treatments are usually required, lasting between 10-30 minutes each, at intervals of 1-2 weeks. As this is such a new treatment, it is unknown how long the effects will last for, but experts are predicting that one course of treatment should last over ten years.

Is it safe?

This is one of the safest lasers as the laser only treats specific areas, and it has been approved by the FDA (the US Food and Drug Administration).

£ PRICE
Around £750 per treatment, or £3,000 for a course of four

TOP TIP

Even when procedures are effective and lasting, experts still recommend that you supplement your treatment with a healthy diet, high water intake and that you avoid sunshine.

'This is something we've been waiting a long time for. Its completely new approach to skin resurfacing allows us to treat areas other lasers cannot touch, such as neck, chest and hands, with minimal healing time. Its results are amazing '

Mr Jan Stanek FRCS cosmetic surgeon and principal of the Wimpole Street clinic

Your skin will naturally and vigorously exfoliate, with flaking similar to that of mild sunburn.

What should I ask?

You should have a thorough consultation to find out whether the Fraxel laser will deliver the results you want, or if you will need an alternative invasive laser treatment. As this treatment is so new, make sure that you find a practitioner who is fully trained and experienced in its use.

Is it right for me?

Clients tend to have this procedure in their twenties for acne scarring and open pores, while those in their late thirties and over undergo it for skin rejuvenation.

Contraindications

Sunbathing and sunbeds should be avoided for several weeks leading up to treatment.

IPL
(INTENSE PULSED LIGHT)

What is it?

Intense pulsed light (IPL) directs short pulses of intense light into the skin, causing it to heat up. This heating causes mild thermal damage, which the skin repairs by producing collagen. The side effect of this increase in collagen production is an improved appearance of the skin texture without removing or damaging the outer layers of the skin.

How it's done

A cold gel is applied to the treatment area and an intense light is then applied in a series of gentle

pulses via a glass handpiece. The light penetrates through the skin and heats up the tissue. Each treatment takes about 30 minutes. There may be some mild stinging during treatment, but this can be avoided by using a local anaesthetic cream.

Time to heal

It is usual for the skin to feel hot afterwards, with redness lasting about an hour. Immediately after treatment you may notice a mild warmth and tingling sensation. This is normal and will subside after a couple of hours. Use a high factor sun block (SPF 30) for four weeks after treatment, as skin will be more prone to sun damage.

How long will the effects last?

Treatment is usually recommended as a series of 3-6 procedures approximately 3-4 weeks apart. For optimum, longer-term results, it is recommended that you have a maintenance programme of two IPL treatments per year.

Is it safe?

The IPL system filters the light carefully so that the harmful shorter wavelengths are removed, while the longer wavelengths are allowed to safely treat the skin. A software programme calculates the right delivery for each skin type, minimising the risk of complications. Complications can sometimes occur, however, and include blistering of the skin, which can very rarely lead to mild scarring and small changes in skin colour.

BEFORE

Skin is smoother and firmer

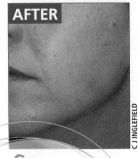

AFTER

C J INGLEFIELD

GOOD FOR?
☑ broken capillaries
☑ uneven pigmentation
☑ broken blood vessels
☑ age spots
☑ melasma (dark facial skin discolouration particularly common in pregnant women)
☑ skin conditions such as rosacea and other minor blemishes
☑ hair removal

TOP 5 PROCEDURES FOR YOUR LUNCH HOUR

THERAPY	HOW LONG?	EFFECTS	PAGE
Botox	10-15 minutes	Smooths fine lines and wrinkles	49
Intense pulsed light (IPL)	30 minutes	Heals broken capillaries, blemishes, age spots, and uneven pigmentation	57
Light therapy	20 minutes	Smooths fine lines and wrinkles	59
Microwave treatment	10-30 minutes	Removes thread veins	60
Perfector	45 minutes	Lifts and firms skin	62

>> IPL (INTENSE PULSED LIGHT)

What should I ask?
Find out if the IPL treatment will be powerful enough to treat your skin problem or if you will need a more invasive treatment. Ask how many sessions you will need and how often you should expect to require follow-up treatments each year.

Is it right for me?
Clients in their thirties upwards generally undertake this procedure for skin conditions such as rosacea, acne and melasma.

Contraindications
If you have been in the sun or on a sunbed you will need to wait at least 4-6 weeks before having IPL. You should not have the treatment if you are pregnant or have used Roaccutane in the six months leading up to treatment.

LIGHT THERAPY

What is it?
Lumière and Omnilux Revive are procedures that use a cosmetic lamp for skin rejuvenation and the prevention of fine lines and wrinkles. They produce pure red light through LED (light emitting diode) technology, which emits the correct wavelength of light to stimulate collagen and elastin production, to keep skin firm and supple. Essentially the procedure converts light energy into cellular building blocks for your skin.

How it's done
The client lies down while a therapist gets the light ready. The device is timed to switch off after the 20-minute procedure has been completed. Although the skin will warm up, this is not a painful procedure.

Time to heal
The skin should instantly appear healthier and glowing with no redness or swelling.

How long will the results last?
Between 6-12 treatments are recommended with monthly or bi-monthly top-ups to maintain results. However, skin should appear more vibrant after just one treatment.

Is it safe?
No infra red or UV rays are used, so the procedure is completely safe. Any adverse reactions would not be permanent. There are no

PHOTO THERAPEUTICS LTD

IPL PRICE
From £100-£500 per area per treatment

LIGHT THERAPY PRICE
Ranges between £35-£50 per treatment

Light therapy warms the skin to keep it supple

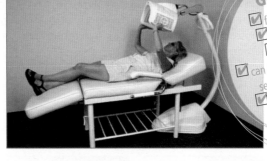

GOOD FOR?
- ☑ fine lines and wrinkles
- ☑ spots and blemishes
- ☑ uneven skin tone
- ☑ can be an effective treatment for seasonal affective disorder
- ☑ can prolong the effects of Botox and fillers

side effects to treatment except where the therapy is contraindicated (see below).

What should I ask?
Will the procedure make a visible difference to your skin problem, or will you need something more invasive? Find out if you will also need fillers to get the full results you want.

Is it right for me?
This procedure is suitable for all age groups and skin types. Someone with sun damaged skin would get more noticeable results.

Contraindications
You must not undertake light therapy if you are light sensitive or on light sensitising medication.

BEFORE

Lines have been smoothed

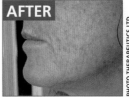

AFTER

PHOTO THERAPEUTICS LTD

>>

MICRO-CURRENT MACHINES

What is it?
Also known as CACI (computer aided cosmetology treatment) or the 'non-surgical face lift', this procedure uses tiny electrical impulses and signals to stimulate muscle tone and enhance skin tissue.

GOOD FOR?
- ☑ fine lines and wrinkles
- ☑ pigmentation and acne scarring
- ☑ sun-damaged skin and blemishes
- ☑ poor circulation
- ☑ face contours
- ☑ poor muscle tone

How it's done
Cotton-tipped probes and pads are placed on the face and body, then tiny micro-currents of electricity are passed through the treatment site. This stimulates the muscles, leading to an increase in protein production, tightening them to restore a firmer shape and tone to the face. The sensation is akin to 'pins and needles' and is merely uncomfortable, rather than painful. It is an hour-long treatment.

Time to heal
There is no healing time involved so you will be able to resume your daily routine immediately.

How long will the effects last?
Results can be seen after 4–5 sessions but it is recommended that you have a course of at least ten treatments followed by monthly maintenance sessions for optimum results.

Is it safe?
The CACI micro-current system has acquired a reputation for being safe, non-invasive and effective. Reassuringly, the machine started out as an approved medical aid. You will feel very little discomfort when the current is applied to your skin, if anything at all. There are no known side effects. Most people feel relaxed and energised following treatment.

What should I ask?
Find out if your problem is too severe to be treated by the CACI machine and whether an invasive method may be necessary for the results you want. You should also find out how many CACI sessions you will need to obtain results.

Is it right for me?
The best candidates for this procedure are age 35 or over.

Contraindications
None.

MICROWAVE TREATMENT (VEINWAVE)

What is it?
Veinwave is a microwave treatment that removes unsightly thin red veins from beneath the skin using a process called thermocoagulation. This process heats the veins in order to destroy them. Although this sounds like quite a daunting prospect, the procedure itself is actually very quick and involves little pain.

How it's done
Using the principle of thermocoagulation, a high frequency microwave is administered via a needle into the vein. This heats it up and destroys it, without affecting the outer layers of the skin or internal elements around it. The body then reabsorbs it. The procedure is slightly uncomfortable as you will feel the heating underneath the skin. A session lasts from 10–30 minutes and 40–50cm of veins can be treated in that time.

GOOD FOR?
- ☑ unsightly, thin veins
- ☑ very fine thread veins, particularly those that are difficult to inject
- ☑ delicate foot areas
- ☑ delicate and sensitiv[e] areas of the face

Time to heal
The treatment leaves no bruising or swelling, though there may be some redness for 3–6 weeks.

CACI
BEFORE AFTER
The muscle tone has been stimulated, making skin tighter

DID YOU KNOW?
Starting life as a medical aid in the late 1980s, the micro-current machine was used to treat facial weakness in palsy victims. It is now also used to help treat muscular injuries in athletes. Since the early 1990s it has been used as a means of administering the 'non surgical face lift.'

£

MICRO-CURRENT PRICE
£40-£60 per treatment session. Multiple sessions can usually be bought at a discount

MICROWAVE TREATMENT PRICE
£150-£250 per session

How long will the effects last?

A single thread vein may require just one treatment session in order for it to disappear, but repeat sessions may be required if multiple areas are affected. According to Veinwave practitioner Brian Newman, 90% of veins that are treated will not recur.

Is it safe?

Complications with this procedure are extremely rare and there is very little chance of scarring following treatment. The procedure has been well-tested and is safe.

What should I ask?

You should ask your consultant how many treatments they think will be needed to remove the veins, as well as finding out if repeat procedures may be necessary in the future.

Is it right for me?

This treatment can be used on all skin types and on clients of any age.

Contraindications

Veinwave is not suitable if you are pregnant, epileptic or are fitted with a pacemaker.

DID YOU KNOW?

● Thread veins affect 55% of women

● 40-50 cm of thread veins can be treated in 10-30 minutes

skin hydrating

Sometimes a healthy dose of the body's own vitamins and nutrients is what is needed. The Mesolift procedure will revitalise and energise your skin with a natural remedy

MESOLIFT

What is it?

A series of injections of nutrients – comprising vitamins, amino acids, minerals, co-enzymes and nucleic acids – that hydrate the skin, improve circulation and speed up the metabolism to smooth wrinkles and tone the skin. The blend of nutrients contains ingredients that promote the skin's natural production of collagen and elastin to firm sagging skin.

How it's done

A series of microinjections is given, possibly with a local anathestic gel. The injections are conducted with a very fine needle, so will only cause minimal discomfort. The procedure initially consists of two treatments spaced a week apart, then four or more further treatments spaced at longer intervals.

Time to heal

The injection sites may be slightly red after the procedure but this will fade over the course of the day. There may be some light bruising. As there is no surgery involved, you may return to your daily routine immediately.

How long will the effects last?

Many clients describe their skin as looking rested,

radiant and glowing after one treatment, although Mesolift is usually performed in a course of 2-6 treatments as the effects are cumulative, with your body slowly developing collagen and elastin over time. It is recommended that you have touch up sessions twice a year to maintain results.

Is it safe?

The treatment is safe because the nutrients being injected are ones that are usually found in our bodies anyway. Our supply of them may have become depleted as a result of sun exposure, hormonal changes, poor diet and poor circulation. The Mesolift treatment itself may leave your skin feeling tight for a couple of days. There is a very small chance of bruising.

What should I ask?

Will the injections be sufficient to restore vitality to your skin or will you need a more invasive procedure to see results? Are there any vitamin supplements that deliver similar ingredients as a substitute or addition to the treatment?

Is it right for me?

This procedure is suitable for people of all ages and skin types.

Contraindications

None.

GOOD FOR?
☑ fine lines and wrinkles on the face
☑ sagging skin on the neck that needs toning and tightening
☑ a good complement to other skin treatments including dermal fillers

MESOLIFT PRICE
£150 per session

>>

NON-INVASIVE

skin firming

Any one of the following all-over skin-firming treatments can help you regain a fresh, youthful complexion quickly and easily

BEFORE

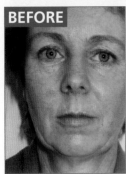

The skin is much less saggy

AFTER

PERFECTOR

PERFECTOR

What is it?
Perfector is an anti-ageing treatment that uses a combination of micro-current, frequency and waveform electric currents. These work on all levels of the skin, soft tissue and muscle fibre to help speed up cellular activity, increase metabolism and re-educate the muscle fibres.

How it's done
The skin is first cleansed and toned, and then a micro-current gel is applied to the treatment area. The Perfector machine resembles a cordless telephone and features two electrodes that deliver the currents to the skin. The machine goes through a series of processes: stimulating circulation, lymphatic drainage to remove toxins, superficial lifting, deep lifting and firming. Some of the sensations may feel like deep massage but the process is not painful. The whole process takes around 45 minutes.

GOOD FOR?
- ☑ lines and wrinkles
- ☑ other lines, especially those around the jaw
- ☑ drooping jowls
- ☑ lifeless cheeks
- ☑ facial contours
- ☑ loose skin

Time to heal
There is no healing time. Makeup can be applied immediately after treatment.

How long will the effects last?
Results can be seen after the first session, although for a dramatic change a full course of 6-10 treatments is recommended, with follow up treatments every six months.

Is it safe?
The treatment is completely safe and non-invasive.

What should I ask?
You should find out how many treatments it will take before you see the results you want.

Is it right for me?
Most candidates for this treatment are over 35.

Contraindications
None.

PURELOGICOL

What is it?
The Purelogicol range consists of a body collagen supplement, facemask, face serum and a lip plumper. Each product contains pure hydrolysed collagen, a high percentage of hyaluronic acid and plant extracts to plump, hydrate and firm the skin while also fighting free radical damage.

How it's done
The great thing about the Purelogicol programme is that it is a DIY treatment that can be done in the comfort of your own home. Twice a week, apply the facemask to the face and neck area and massage in until absorbed. Leave for 10-15 minutes then wash off. Finish by applying Purelogicol collagen velvet serum. Supplement this by taking two Purelogicol capsules at night before bedtime. This is a relaxing process that involves no discomfort whatsoever.

Time to heal
The whole process is a gradual one, but there is no bruising or swelling involved, so therefore no healing period.

How long will the effects last?
The effects are gradual and will build up over time. The results will continue to last as long as you continue to follow the Purelogicol programme.

Is it safe?
Purelogicol is formulated without the inclusion of parabens, perfume, alcohol or colours, so it is totally hypoallergenic and suitable for all skin types. There are no known side effects.

Best candidates
Most candidates who follow this programme are aged between 30-60 years.

Contrad-indications
None.

GOOD FOR?
- ☑ fine lines and wrinkles
- ☑ lax or loose skin
- ☑ cellulite
- ☑ general well-being

It can also help strengthen:
- ☑ weak nails and thin hair
- ☑ joints

£

PERFECTOR PRICE
From £45 per treatment

PURELOGICOL PRICE
Purelogicol Collagen Face Mask (12 x applications) £44.99; Purelogicol Velvet Face Serum (30ml) £39.99; Purelogicol Collagen Body Supplement (1 month supply) £29.99; Purelogicol PurePout Lip Plumper (7ml) and Lip Exfoliator (10ml) £24.50

BEFORE

Thermage has tightened the skin and smoothed the lines

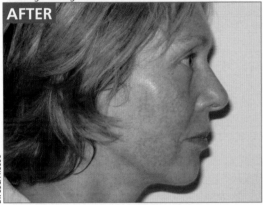

AFTER

DR LUCA RUSSO

'50% of my patients have an immediate, dramatic effect after just one treatment. In many cases just one treatment is enough, with a touch-up six months later to maintain the great result '

Dr Mario Luca Russo MD The Rejuvenation Clinic

THERMAGE (THERMACOOL)

What is it?
A non-surgical treatment that transfers radio frequency deep into the skin, heating the collagen and causing it to tighten, while also kick-starting the production of new collagen.

How it's done
Radio frequencies are passed through a hand-held Thermatip device, to warm large volumes of collagen within the deeper layers of the skin, while at the same time protecting outer layers by cooling. The heated collagen fibres tighten to lift and contour the skin. The heating can be uncomfortable on less fleshy areas, such as the jaw, but is not painful and an anaesthestic cream can be applied. The treatment takes up to an hour to administer.

GOOD FOR?
- ☑ loose or sagging skin on the face, neck and body
- ☑ poorly contoured areas
- ☑ acne scars
- ☑ fine lines
- ☑ moderate wrinkles
- ☑ oily skin

Time to heal
There is no real healing time involved, although the skin may look slightly red for 2-3 hours.

How long will the effects last?
For 30% of patients, a mild immediate tightening is seen after one treatment, with sustained improvement expected within 2-6 months as the natural production of new collagen is catalysed. Results can last up to five years depending on the individual.

Is it safe?
Thermage has been approved by the FDA (US Food and Drug Administration) and can be performed on all ages and skin types. Risks include swelling, bumps and blisters on or around the area treated, usually disappearing within a few days. Very rare permanent side effects are skin indentations or dimpling.

What should I ask?
Which areas should I have treated? Will the results last or will I need top-up treatments?

Is it right for me?
Candidates are typically 35 and older.

Contraindications
Pregnancy, breast-feeding, having a pacemaker or metallic implants in your face (dental fillers are fine). Wait six months after chemical peels, dermal fillers or a course of Roaccutane.

DID YOU KNOW?

● Collagen is the most abundant protein in the body, accounting for 85% of skin, hair, nail and joint tissue
● From the age of 25, collagen depletes at a rate of 1.5% every year
● After this age, most people begin to notice the appearance of fine lines and loss of skin elasticity

---

£ **THERMAGE PRICE**
From £1,500-£4,000 per area per treatment

THE BODY

As we age, we tend to suffer from poor circulation which leads to an accumulation of fat and localised cellulite. Unfortunately, women tend to suffer from this problem more than men, as our bodies contain a higher number of fatty cells. Cellulite and areas of stubborn fat may be a hereditary problem or could be due to hormonal problems, bad habits, a sedentary lifestyle or stress. Whatever the cause, we have researched the methods for reviving the body's circulation to help you rid the body of stubborn fat, leaving you looking and feeling slimmer and younger. Read on and you'll also find out how to get bigger, perkier breasts without going under the surgeons knife.

BEAUTYTEK

What is it?

Best used for the treatment of cellulite, Beautytek is a body sculpting technique incorporating electrical energy, state of the art technology and traditional Chinese theories of well-being. A low-frequency electrical impulse is passed into the body to achieve energetic balance. Beautytek encourages the transfer of fat out of the fat cells so that it can be burned as energy. Existing cellulite is broken down and the body's metabolism is increased to repair cells, produce collagen and sustain the results for a much longer period of time.

How it's done

An electrolyte gel will be applied and a therapist will pass a conductive hand-held probe over the treatment area. At certain points, similar to those used in acupuncture, a transfer of energy will be activated, to enhance the self-repair mechanisms of your body. You are given a conductor to hold so that the Beautytek machine can measure your response and calculate the electrical stimulus required to balance the body. The treatment is only as painful as pins and needles and you will get used to the sensation over the course of the treatment. Typically, a session will last around 60 minutes, although the face and leg treatments will take longer.

Time to heal

No healing time is required.

What results can I expect?

Whilst results can be seen after a single treatment, a series of twelve treatments, with two treatments per week and at least a day between each treatment, will typically show dramatic results. Once the desired result has been achieved, maintenance treatments are recommended every three to four months.

Is it safe?

Some clients feel a tingling sensation as the current passes through the wand, although this is not painful. During and after treatment you may feel the urge to go to the toilet frequently. This is perfectly normal and indicates that the treatment is having the desired effect. The procedure is very safe, as the software calculates the precise electrical stimulus required for the client in question to become balanced.

What should I ask?

How many sessions will I need to see a result? Am I too overweight for the treatment to work? Will I need to adopt a new exercise and diet programme to complement the treatment?

Is it right for me?

Suitable for slightly overweight people of all ages.

Contraindications

Pregnancy, breast-feeding, pacemakers, epilepsy or cancer within the last five years. Clients with large metal implants such as artificial hips cannot be treated in the specific area of the prosthesis.

BRAVA

What is it?

Brava is a DIY procedure that can be done from home, that grows a woman's natural breast tissue. The Brava system consists of two semi-rigid domes with silicone gel rims and a sophisticated pump called a SmartBox, which creates and regulates the tension within the domes. A sports bra is also included to keep these in place.

How it's done

Domes are placed over the breasts and secured in place with the sports bra. A small pump takes the air out of the domes to create a vacuum, which applies a gentle three-dimensional pull on the breast. When the tension is sustained the cells respond by reproducing, causing the breast tissue to grow. The SmartBox is a matchbox-sized computer which regulates the level of pressure.

Time to heal

There is no healing time as Brava is a gradual process.

Pressure is digitally-regulated

GOOD FOR?

- ☑ cellulite
- ☑ lax skin
- ☑ the unfirm underlying tissue below skin
- ☑ stretch marks
- ☑ water retention
- ☑ general well-being

GOOD FOR?

- ☑ small breasts
- ☑ breasts that have lost their shape
- ☑ breasts without fullness
- ☑ ideal for women who wish to regain their breast shape and size after childbirth and breast-feeding

BEAUTYTEK PRICE

From £150 per session

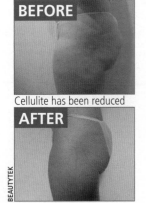

BEFORE

Cellulite has been reduced

AFTER

BEAUTYTEK

BRAVA UK

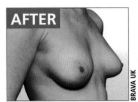

The results will start to show after 15 weeks of treatment

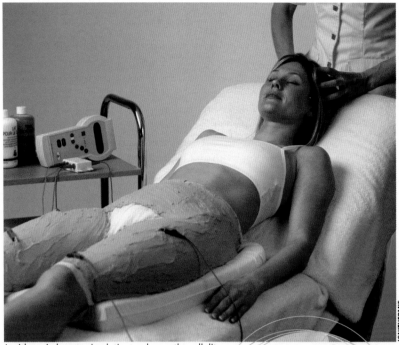

Ionithermie boosts circulation and smooths cellulite

What results can I expect?

For the system to work, it must be worn for 11 or more consecutive hours each day for a minimum of 15 consecutive weeks. It is imperative that the non-wear period between Brava sessions does not exceed 13 hours. The results will slowly start to show over the 15-week course of treatment. After this time, you will find a sustained increase in breast size of at least one cup size.

Is it safe?

Yes. The domes you get are selected specifically for you and the SmartBox regulates the optimal pressure you should experience.

What should I ask?

Ensure that you have the correct measurements taken, so that you get the appropriate domes for your height, width and breast size.

Is it right for me?

It is suitable for women who are healthy and over 18, with breasts that measure an AA, A, B or small C cup.

Contraindications

This procedure is not suitable for women who are a C cup or above.

IONITHERMIE

What is it?

This is a hip and thigh sculpting procedure that will firm skin, and smooth cellulite. It combines electric currents, thermal clay and micronised algae to boost the metabolism and tone muscles.

How it's done

First, a body scrub boosts circulation and sweeps away dead skin cells. A thermal clay and algae mask is then applied. Pads are placed on the outer thighs and knees and rhythmic electrical pulses are passed through these pads for 30 minutes, after which the hardened clay mask is peeled off. The treatment is not painful but the electrical pulses may sting at first. The treatment takes 75 minutes.

Time to heal

The treatment can leave a pinkish tone to the skin but this disappears quickly.

What result can I expect?

You can see results after one treatment but for the best results a course of five is recommended. After a course, your skin will be smooth and toned with reduced cellulite and overall body inch loss of 1-8 inches. The results are lasting, if you maintain a sensible diet and exercise programme.

Is it safe?

Yes, although you may experience slight detox symptoms such as a headache, so you should drink lots of water before and after treatment.

What should I ask?

How many treatments will I need to have?

Is it right for me?

The best candidates are over 30 and slightly overweight. It is ideal for dieters who have managed to successfully shed the pounds but now need to tone and firm.

Contraindications

Metal pins and plates, a history of cancer in the family, liver or kidney problems, pregnancy, breast-feeding, recent surgery, pacemaker or epilepsy.

GOOD FOR?
- ☑ inch loss
- ☑ skin toning
- ☑ hips, knees and thighs
- ☑ stomachs
- ☑ low energy levels
- ☑ cellulite
- ☑ detoxing the body

BRAVA PRICE
£1,195 including p&p

IONITHERMIE PRICE
£45-£60 per session

DID YOU KNOW?

● 80% of women in Western Europe believe they have cellulite

● Cellulite is referred to as cottage cheese skin and orange peel skin

● Cellulite is a series of fat cells and fibrous tissue which has 'rippled' under the skin

● Although it is more obvious in overweight women, thinner women are also susceptible, as everyone stores fat under their skin

MESOTHERAPY

What is it?
Hyaluronic acid (HA), which is naturally present in the skin, helps transport essential nutrients from the bloodstream to the skin cells and hydrates the skin by holding in water. As skin ages, the amount of HA in the skin decreases, which can contribute to loss of skin elasticity. Mesotherapy directly injects HA into large areas of skin to leave it smooth and hydrated.

How it's done
Injections of small amounts of HA are administered beneath the skin to break down fatty deposits. The procedure lasts 10-30 minutes depending on the size of the treated area. The injections are done using extremely small needles and only penetrate to a very small depth, typically 4-6mm so, while the procedure can be uncomfortable, it is not painful and you will not be left with any visible marks.

Time to heal
There can be redness, swelling, pain, itching or tenderness at the injection site for 1-2 days. Small bruises may appear, but these will disappear gradually in the first few days after treatment.

What results can I expect?
The appearance of results is gradual, with a noticeable reduction of fat occurring over the course of 5 treatments (10 or more for cellulite). Generally, 2-3 treatments every 4-6 weeks are recommended. As the HA is gradually broken down within the skin over a few months, it is a good idea to have maintenance treatments every 4-6 months.

Is it safe?
Hypersensitivity to HA has been reported in about 1 in 10,000 treated people, but the side effects of this will only last 1-2 weeks. On the whole, reactions are extremely rare and the procedure is considered safe.

What should I ask?
How soon will I see results? How many treatments will I need? Am I too overweight for the treatment to be effective?

Is it right for me?
It suits patients who are slightly overweight best.

GOOD FOR?
☑ dehydrated skin
☑ cellulite
☑ body sculpting
☑ poor skin tone
☑ thighs
☑ buttocks
☑ back and stomach

£ MESOTHERAPY PRICE
£200-£300 per treatment session. Discounts are usually offered for a course

Contraindications
Cancer, pregnancy, heart disease. It is not effective in treating loose or hanging skin.

SCLEROTHERAPY (VASCULIGHT)

What is it?
Sclerotherapy removes thread or spider veins by injecting them with a solution that causes the vein walls to swell and gradually disappear over the course of a few weeks. This treatment is mainly used for thread and spider veins, which are the fine red veins near to the surface of the skin. The treatment is not appropriate for use on varicose veins (which tend to be thicker, deeper and blue in colour), as these are usually caused by underlying leg pump failure.

How it's done
Sclerotherapy involves injecting a solution into the unwanted leg vein using a very fine needle. The solution, usually a mixture of sterile salt and local anaesthetic, acts as an irritant and causes the wall of the vein to collapse and disperse naturally. The injections can be slightly painful but are over quickly. The sensation can be described as the touch of a warm needle. The treatment takes around 15 minutes depending on the size of the area to be treated.

Time to heal
Afterwards there will be some bruising and maybe minimal swelling for 2-4 weeks. Patients should avoid hot drinks, alcohol, spicy foods and exercise for several days after treatment. For 4-8 weeks, veins may look more prominent (fading gradually) and the injection site may itch.

What results can I expect?
Most people require 2-6 treatments at 4-8 week intervals, depending on the size of the thread veins. Results can be seen after about four weeks, and a 75% disappearance of the veins is expected.

GOOD FOR?
☑ unsightly leg thread veins
☑ veins on the calves and thighs
☑ port wine stains (reddish-purplish skin discolouration)
☑ spider veins
☑ rosacea
☑ overly pink scars

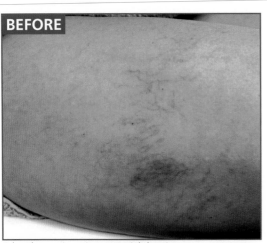

BEFORE

Sclerotherapy in action on unsightly veins

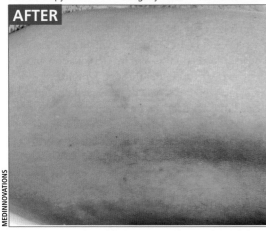

AFTER

MEDINNOVATIONS

However, there is always the possibility that new veins will develop later.

Is it safe?
In the UK, only a specifically trained laser doctor or nurse is allowed to perform vascular laser treatments. Serious complications are very rare although superficial burns, inflammation, ulcers and scarring or pigmentation problems do occasionally occur.

What should I ask?
Should I have an ultrasound first to ensure I don't have leg pump failure? How many treatments will I need to cover the affected area?

Is it right for me?
Patients of any age can be treated.

Contraindications
Sunburn to the area, recent tanning of the treatment area, very dark skin, diabetes, photosensitivity or the taking of photosensitising medication, or pregnancy and breast-feeding.

ULTRASHAPE

What is it?
Ultrashape is known as 'non-surgical liposuction', and is designed for ultrasonic body sculpturing. It uses a focused ultrasound that selectively breaks down fat cells, while still protecting the skin, nerves and blood vessels in order to reduce or contour areas of the body. It is especially useful on troublesome fatty areas that have proved to be resistant to sensible diet and exercise, and will correct problems around the abdomen, hips and thighs.

How it's done
Your physician will start by marking out the treatment area. Then, you will be asked to lie back on a bed, while the practitioner uses a round hand-held device to deliver ultrasound beams gently over the marked region of your body. During treatment, the beam of focused ultrasound energy will penetrate the treatment area and selectively destroy fat cells, while having no effect on skin, blood vessels and nerves. The entire procedure is guided by innovative tracking technology that ensures smooth, safe, uniform contouring, and is very straightforward. The skin may feel warm and slightly uncomfortable during treatment, although it will not be painful. The procedure takes between 45-90 minutes, and the size of the area to be treated will determine its length.

Time to heal
You should expect some mild discomfort in the early stages if bruising occurs, although this is extremely rare and is only very mild. As there is no trauma to the tissues, you will not need any healing time and can return to your normal routine straight away.

GOOD FOR?
☑ troublesome fatty areas that are resistant to diet and exercise
☑ abdomen, hips and thighs
☑ love handles
☑ poor body contour
☑ assymetry or irregularity of the lips

£ **SCLEROTHERAPY PRICE**
From £150-£1,895 for a full leg treatment

TOP PROCEDURES FOR YOUR LUNCH HOUR

THERAPY	HOW LONG?	EFFECTS	PAGE
Beautytek	60 minutes	Breaks down cellulite	66
Mesotherapy	10-30 minutes	Rehydrates and smooths skin	68
Sclerotherapy	15 minutes	Removes varicose and thread veins	68
VelaSmooth	20 minutes	Breaks down cellulite	70

>>

>> ULTRASHAPE

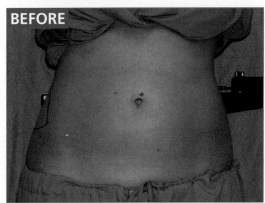

BEFORE

Ultrashape has resculpted and firmed the tummy area

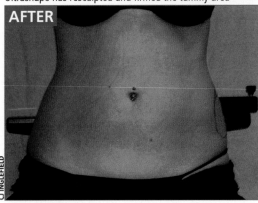

AFTER

CJ INGLEFIELD

What results can I expect?
Ultrashape treatment provides a safe and effective reduction in body fat that is long lasting. Multiple treatments may be required to address several areas of the body.

Is it safe?
Blistering is rare and, if it does occur, usually heals within a couple of days. On the whole, the treatment is considered to be safe.

What should I ask?
Will I need to lose any weight before the procedure? How many treatments will I need? Which areas should I have treated?

Is it right for me?
You should only weigh up to approximately 6kg over the ideal weight for your height. This is not a treatment for obesity.

Contraindications
Pregnancy, chronic metabolic disease, a pacemaker, a history of blood coagulation disorder, being HIV-positive, having an abdominal hernia, taking aspirin or NSAID (non-steroidal anti-inflammatory drug) in the last ten days, Vitamin E in the last week, or exposure to pesticides.

£ ULTRASHAPE PRICE
From £150

VELASMOOTH PRICE
£80-£120 per 45-minute treatment

VELASMOOTH

What is it?
VelaSmooth is a laser-like medical tool which uses a simultaneous combination of heat, deep tissue massage and suction to safely and effectively reduce the appearance of cellulite.

GOOD FOR?
☑ cellulite
☑ dimpled skin
☑ hips
☑ thighs
☑ poor body contouring
☑ poor circulation

How it's done
VelaSmooth mechanically massages the treatment area, and uses infrared light (which generates heat to mobilise fat cells) and radio frequency (which aids new collagen formation) to improve circulation and remove toxins and fluid through lymphatic drainage, which is a type of massage. The tool is placed directly over the treatment area and you will feel a pinching sensation as the suction gets to work. Your skin may also feel slightly warm after treatment. A session takes up to one hour, depending on the size of the area being treated.

Time to heal
Redness and mild bruising may occur in the treated area but this is rare and will disappear within a day. You will not need to take any time off or make changes to your routine.

What results can I expect?
Recent clinical trials show a 70% improvement in the appearance of cellulite. Patients with grade three cellulite (obvious on standing) require ten or more treatments, but results should start to show after around 6 treatments. Patients get an average hip size reduction of 3-5cm and an improvement in the texture and contouring of skin. It is recommended to have two treatments per week for four weeks initially, and then have a maintenance treatment once every three months to maintain results.

Is it safe?
This procedure has been well-tested and is safe. The only very rare complications include minor burns. The lymph system is stimulated by this procedure, so it is important that you drink at least two litres of water a day during treatment to aid the removal of toxins, which will leave skin looking brighter, tighter and more hydrated.

>> VELASMOOTH CASE STUDY

Patient: Rebecca, 38, dental nurse
Type of treatment: cellulite reduction
Brand: VelaSmooth
Area of treatment: thighs

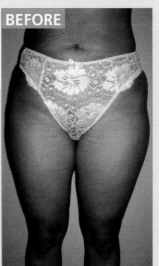

BEFORE   AFTER

The dimpled skin has been reduced and her thighs are much smoother

WIGMORE

Q Why did you choose this particular treatment?
A I am not particularly overweight but have suffered from really dimpled skin on my thighs for years. It's made me feel really awkward and nervous about things like wearing swimming costumes. No amount of diet or exercise has ever shifted the cellulite and I was not keen on the idea of surgery, so I did some research and found out about VelaSmooth. It seemed like the right choice as it is quick, safe and involves no recovery time – an essential factor for a busy mum.

Q Where did you go for treatment and who administered it?
A Dr Patrick Treacy at the Ailesbury Clinic in Dublin.

Q How long did your treatment take?
A I am following a course of eight 45-minute treatments and will continue to have maintenance treatments once every three months when the course is over.

Q How did you feel during and after treatment, and how did you look immediately afterwards?
A The procedure involves a suction device that feels like someone pinching your skin. It is slightly uncomfortable at first but not painful. After one treatment I could really feel the results: my circulation had improved and the skin on my legs felt slightly tighter. I've had six of my eight treatments and my clothes are starting to feel looser.

Q Did you suffer any negative side effects?
A None at all.

Q Were you immediately satisfied, or did it take time to see the full benefits?
A As you need a course of treatments, the effect is gradual rather than immediate, but I could feel a difference after the first session. Once my course is complete I think I will see an even bigger improvement. I am really pleased with how things are going so far.

Q What impact has the treatment had on your life?
A As a result of having the VelaSmooth treatments, I have been motivated to eat healthily and exercise more to optimise the results. I am feeling so much happier in myself now, and I now love going shopping for clothes I would never have considered wearing before.

Q Do you have any advice for someone considering this treatment?
A I would definitely recommend the treatment to other people. Not only have I noticed and been pleased with the difference in myself but other people have too. I think the treatment is well worth the money for the fantastic results and the added self-confidence I have gained.

What should I ask?
Ask if you will need to combine treatments with a specific diet/exercise programme to see results. You should also ask how many sessions you will need to see the effect you want.

Is it right for me?
This is good for anyone with visible cellulite.

Contraindications
Pregnancy, scarring or infection of the treatment area, pacemaker, diabetes (Type I or II), photosensitising drugs and agents for known anticoagulative or thromboembolic conditions, use of non-steroidal anti-inflammatory drugs or aspirin within two weeks prior to treatment and any known photosensitivity.

TOP 3 'NO-NEEDLES' TREATMENTS

THERAPY	METHOD	EFFECTS	PAGE
Brava	Provides domes to place over the breasts and create a vacuum that gently pulls on the breasts	Promotes the growth of new breast tissue, thus enlarging the breasts	66
VelaSmooth	Applies a focused ultrasound to treatment area	Breaks down fat, restoring or enhancing body contours	70
Ultrashape	Ultrasound massage with laser-like medical tool	Breaks down cellulite	69

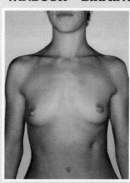 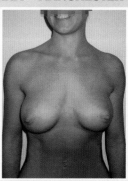
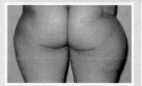 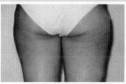
   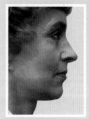
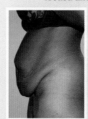 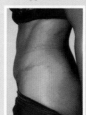  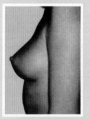

4

the face

COSMETIC SURGERY

When it comes to looking younger, the face is arguably the most important part of the body. Forever on show yet constantly exposed to the elements, including sun damage and pollution, over time the face can begin to look tired and worn. It will come as no surprise to learn that around 50% of cosmetic procedures are carried out on the face, mostly on women rather than men, seeking to look as young as they feel. As cosmetic surgery becomes more acceptable this figure is increasing all the time.

As women are focusing on their careers for longer, starting families later and remaining active well into their sixties and seventies, the pressure to keep looking younger has increased

face value
COSMETIC SURGERY FOR THE FACE

QUESTIONS TO ASK

- Is this the right procedure for me?
- Is there an alternative procedure?
- How much will the hospital fees be?
- What is your complication rate?
- Can I see before and after pictures?
- Will you correct any potential problems?
- How often do you carry out this procedure?
- What is your insurance policy?

COSMETIC SURGERY HAS been so well documented in recent years that, for many, having a nose job, chin tuck or face lift is as acceptable and normal as heading to the high street for a shopping spree. In 2004, 15,019 operations were carried out by members of BAAPS (the British Association of Aesthetic Plastic Surgeons), compared to 9,916 in 2003. 2,273 of these were for eyelid surgery and 1,604 were for face and neck lifts.

Rather than encouraging teenagers, the biggest growth in interest in cosmetic surgery comes from women in their thirties and older. As women are focusing on their careers for longer, starting families later and remaining active well into their sixties and seventies, the pressure to keep looking younger has increased.

It can be hard to know where to start. Cosmetic surgeon Laurence Kirwan (FRCS) says that many types of procedure produce the best results when combined. 'It's like decorating a home,' he says. 'If you put the wallpaper up but don't paint the rim you don't get the results.' Surgeons who suggest you combine treatments are usually acting in your best interests, rather than simply trying to make more money. 'You can save thousands by combining treatments,' says Laurence. 'If you just have one procedure and later realise you'd needed another, you'd have to take more time off work and pay the hospital fees a second time.'

One of the biggest problems is when surgeons misjudge the results that patients are expecting. Good communication at the initial consultation is essential to make sure the surgeon understands what you are looking for, and you know what you can realistically expect.

Jan Stanek, the surgeon featured on the TV series *Ten Years Younger*, advises women to see several surgeons and not to be swayed by flashy advertisements. 'You need to like a surgeon and you need to go by reputation,' he says, recommending that you ask for before and after photos, ask how often the surgeons perform the procedure, and check that their insurance policy is reliable.

Read on to find out what the main types of facial surgical procedures involve: the benefits, risks, prices and, most importantly, the results you can expect.

YOUR GUIDE TO THE RANGE AND TYPE OF PROCEDURES >>

COSMETIC SURGERY

smoother forehead

Having a forehead lift might seem like a trivial piece of work to have done, but in fact it can dramatically alter the way your face looks

BEFORE
The forehead is far smoother

AFTER

LAURENCE KIRWAN

ƒ

FOREHEAD LIFT/ BROW LIFT/ PRICE
£3,000-£4,000

FOREHEAD LIFT/BROW LIFT

What is it?
A forehead or brow lift involves subtle lifting of the forehead to remove lines, wrinkles and sagging skin and is often combined with the removal of underlying muscle and tissue.

How it's done
A traditional forehead lift is referred to as the 'open' technique and involves one long incision to allow the surgeon to reduce or release the muscles. It lasts for 1-2 hours. The endoscopic brow lift involves several inch-long incisions behind the hairline so that the endoscope, which is connected to a tiny camera, can be inserted to give the surgeon a clear view of the muscle and tissue. This surgery lasts for about an hour.

Forehead lifts can be performed under either a general or local anaesthetic.

Time to heal
You should expect pain for several days, with swelling at its worst in the first 24-48 hours. Bruising and numbness will last for a few weeks. Most patients are back to work within two weeks, and full results are visible after about 2-3 months.

Is there scarring?
The operation scars will be permanent but fade over 3-6 months and are usually hidden by hair or by the natural creases in the skin.

How long will the effects last?
Results last 5-10 years.

Is it safe?
You may suffer from headaches if your stitches are too tight. There may also be numbness in the face that lasts a few weeks. In rare cases, this is permanent. Any temporary hair loss, swelling, nerve damage and tightening resolve themselves in three months.

Is it right for me?
Patients tend to be between 30-60 years old.

What should I ask?
Is there an alternative procedure I should have?

HEALING TIME
Swelling is bad for the first 24-48 hours. Most patients are back to work within two weeks.

plumper cheeks

BEFORE

The cheek implants give her face a plumper, younger shape

AFTER

LUCY GLANCEY

Ageing can cause the cheeks to appear sunken and gaunt. Cheek implants could be just the thing to restore their youthfulness

CHEEK IMPLANTS/AUGMENTATION

What is it?
This procedure inserts implants into the cheeks to create a youthful appearance.

How it's done
The surgery can be done either under local or general anaesthetic. The implant is placed over the cheekbone or in the mid-cheek region to fill out sunken areas through an incision made inside the mouth or through an opening just beneath the lower eyelashes. The operation lasts between 30 minutes and two hours.

Time to heal
You should expect considerable swelling, pain and difficulty talking or smiling for several days. Swelling and numbness will ease within a week. You can return to work 2-7 days after surgery.

Is there scarring?
None if the incision is inside the mouth. Incisions beneath the lower lashes cause minimal scarring.

HEALING TIME
Swelling is bad for several days. You will be able to return to work after 2-7 days.

How long will the effects last?
Results are permanent, unless you have a non-permanent implant which will need replacing.

Is it safe?
Some people think they have received too much implant material at first but it can take several months for the swelling to go down. Implants can also be repositioned if the face looks asymmetrical or if they move out of place.

Is it right for me?
Patients tend to be 30+.

What should I ask?
Which type of implant do you recommend?

£ CHEEK IMPLANTS/ AUGMENTATION PRICE
£1,500-£3,000

CHEEK REDUCTION (BUCCAL FAT REMOVAL)

What is it?
This procedure will reduce excess fat around the cheeks, making your cheeks look tighter.

How it's done
This hour-long procedure can be conducted either under general or local anaesthetic and involves making an incision between the cheek and gums, towards the back of the mouth. The muscle is dissected to allow the removal of buccal fat (ie fat from the cheeks) through the incision, which is then closed and sealed with antiseptic-soaked gauze.

Healing time
There will be discomfort for several weeks with swelling and bruising. Care must be taken initially when eating and brushing your teeth, as the scarring will be inside the mouth. You may also experience some tingling, burning and cold sensations for a few weeks.

Is there scarring?
No – incisions are made inside the mouth.

How long will the effects last?
Up to 5-10 years.

Is it safe?
Rare complications include infection, reaction to the anaesthetic, asymmetry of the face, haematoma (blood clots), numbness and puckering of the skin.

Is it right for me?
Adult patients are of all ages.

What should I ask?
Should I wait for my cheeks to recede naturally?

HEALING TIME
There will be swelling and bruising at first but this will disappear after two weeks.

£ CHEEK REDUCTION PRICE
£1,500-£3,000

youthful chin

A chin implant might help to define your lower face better, giving you a more youthful profile. Some implants are permanent, so your new look could last forever...

CHIN IMPLANT (MENTOPLASTY)

What is it?
The chin can recede with age making the face look out of proportion with the neck. An implant can correct this by creating a more youthful appearance with minimal or no scarring. A better-structured chin can make a dramatic difference to the face. Implants can be permanent or temporary.

How it's done
This procedure is usually carried out under general anaesthetic, which would require you to be in hospital overnight, although it depends on the size of the area being treated and the type of implant used. Your surgeon will advise you on this. During the procedure, the chosen implant is inserted via incisions made inside the mouth or on either side of the lower lip. Some surgeons will use an incision point directly under the chin. A pocket is created, into which a lower-jaw implant can be placed. Cuts under the skin are closed with dissolving stitches and incisions on the outside are usually bound with removable stitches.

BEFORE
The chin is more pronounced

AFTER

LUCIAN ION

>>

Time to heal
Swelling and bruising may make smiling and talking painful for several days, but most swelling will have improved in a week and you can normally return to work between 2 and 7 days after the operation. Temporary numbness of the lower lip after surgery is common. You should treat the jaw area gently and avoid disturbing the implant or resting your chin on your hand while you are recovering. Swelling and numbness may take several months to subside entirely before the final shape of the chin is apparent.

Is there scarring?
A tiny scar may be visible if the incision is made underneath the chin but this will fade with time.

How long will the effects last?
Some implants are not permanent and will need replacing. However, a PTFE or an ePTFE implant is permanent. Both are made of a carbon and fluorine-based polymer, which never shrinks and is not absorbed by the body.

Is it safe?
Possible complications can include infection, reaction to anaesthesia, haematoma and nerve damage, but these are rare. A chin implant may not become fixed to the underlying bone and consequently feel unstable, although this is unlikely to have any effect on your appearance. Also, occasionally the outline of the implant can be visible and you may find that your chin creases unnaturally when you smile. There is also a small risk that the lower part of the lip may remain permanently numb and the muscles around the mouth may be weakened.

Is it right for me?
Anyone can have this operation done. Arrange a consultation to discuss your expectations and what results you want.

What should I ask?
What type of implant is best for me? Are there any alternative non-invasive treatments? How many chin implant procedures do you carry out?

HEALING TIME
Swelling and bruising improves after a week. You can return to work 2-7 days after surgery.

CHIN IMPLANT PRICE
£1,500-£3,000

sparkling eyes

Bright eyes are often the first quality we pick out in the faces of strangers. To get your eyes to fulfil their 'sparkle' potential, you may want to consider one of these procedures

UPPER EYE LIFT (UPPER BLEPHAROPLASTY)

What is it?
Eyelid surgery – with someone making incisions incredibly close to your eye – may seem like a fairly unpleasant process, but lifting drooping or hooded upper eyelids and restoring the smooth line of the upper lid can light up your eyes dramatically and make tired, sad eyes look fresh and alert.

How it's done
The surgeon will make an incision into the natural crease above the eyelashes. The skin is then separated, excess fat is removed, sagging muscle and skin are trimmed back and the incisions are closed up. Surgery lasts for around an hour for upper lids and up to two and a half hours for combined upper and lower lid surgery. Blepharoplasty is normally carried out under local anaesthetic, although some patients are given sedation via an intravenous drip.

Healing time
The surgeon will usually lubricate the eyes with an ointment and apply a bandage after surgery. Sutures are removed after five days and bruising will subside after 10 days.

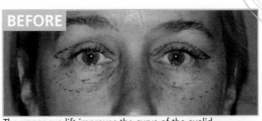
The upper eye lift improves the curve of the eyelid
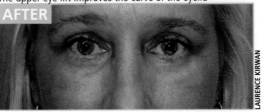

HEALING TIME
Swelling will subside within 10 days, and most people return to work 7-10 days after surgery.

LAURENCE KIRWAN

>>

>> UPPER EYE LIFT

Most people return to work a week to 10 days after surgery, but are instructed to avoid strenuous activity for three weeks. It can take up to three months before full results are complete.

Will there be scarring?

There will be a small scar in the crease or side of the eyelid, however scarring is not very obvious. This will reduce with time and can be easily concealed with make-up.

How long will the effects last?

Refreshed eyes and a more youthful appearance will last for 10-15 years. You may feel that you never need to repeat surgery.

Is it safe?

Possible temporary complications include blurred vision, increased tear production, dry gritty eyes and sometimes a difficulty closing the eyelids, as well as infection, reaction to anaesthetic, nerve damage and asymmetry of the eyes. None of these is permanent, however, and occurrences are rare.

Is it right for me?

Ideal candidates are normally at least 30.

What should I ask?

Do I need lower lid surgery as well? Should I be combining the two procedures?

£ UPPER EYE LIFT PRICE
£1,500-£2,500 for upper eyelid surgery. (£3,000-£4,000 for upper and lower lid surgery combined).

How it's done

The surgeon makes a direct cut under the lower lashes or on the inner side of the lower lid, then lifts the skin and muscle, removes a small amount of fat and trims the excess skin and muscle away. In a newer procedure called a SOOF lift (sub-orbicularis oculi fat lift), however, the fat is put behind the muscle rather than removed, so as to prevent the risk of eyes taking on a sunken appearance. Lower lid surgery takes around an hour. Upper and lower lid surgery combined can take up to two and a half hours. Blepharoplasty is normally carried out under local anaesthetic, but some patients are sedated via an intravenous drip. General anaesthetic is rarely used.

Time to heal

After the procedure, the surgeon will usually lubricate the eyes with an ointment and apply a bandage. The stitches will be removed after around five days, and bruising and swelling will subside after the first 10 days. Most people return to work between a week and 10 days after surgery, but are instructed to avoid strenuous activity for the first three weeks after surgery. It can take up to three months before the full results are visible.

EYEBAG RECONTOURING (LOWER BLEPHAROPLASTY)

What is it?

The skin loses its elasticity over time and muscles slacken with age. When this happens around the lower eye area, you can be left looking tired, worn and older than you should. Eyebag recontouring (also known as lower eyelid blepharoplasty or lower lid surgery) refreshes the eyes by reducing puffy bags and excess folds beneath the eyelashes, giving you a more youthful appearance. Eyebag recontouring cannot, however, remove dark circles under the eyes, lift sagging eyebrows or smooth wrinkles around the eyes. In this case, chemical peels may be suggested to correct sun damage, fine lines and wrinkles, while a brow lift will correct sagging eyebrows.

HEALING TIME
Swelling will subside within 10 days, and most people return to work 7-10 days after surgery.

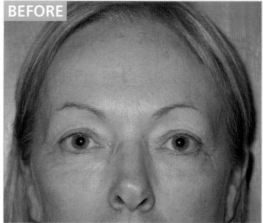

BEFORE

The eyebag recontouring makes her eyes stand out more

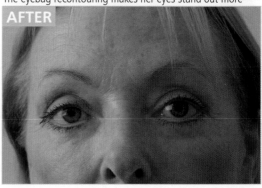

AFTER

ANGELICA KAVOUNI

Is there scarring?

There can be minimal scarring that fades over time, although there is no scarring at all if the incision is made within the lower lid.

How long will the effects last?

The more youthful appearance set off by your revitalised eyes will last between 10 and 15 years, and so may never need to be redone.

Is it safe?

Temporary side effects can include blurred vision, increased tear production, dry gritty eyes and sometimes a difficulty closing the eyelids. Infection, reaction to anaesthetic, nerve damage, bleeding and asymmetry of the eyes are also possible. Contact lens wearers may have to wear glasses for some weeks after surgery.

Is this right for me?

Patients are typically over the age of 30, although people who have the familial problem of bags beneath the eyes may undergo surgery in their twenties. It is best to discuss all the options with your GP or consultant, so they can recommend the best course of action to take.

What should I ask?

Do I need to have upper lid surgery as well? How many of these procedures have you carried out? Can I look at before and after pictures? Should I be combining this with another procedure to optimise the results? How long will it last? At what point will I need to repeat surgery?

EYEBAG RECONTOURING PRICE
£2,000-£3,000 for lower eyelid surgery, £3,000-£4,000 for upper and lower lid surgery combined.

DID YOU KNOW?

● Cosmetic surgeons will charge a normal consultation fee just like any other specialist. You will be asking for their professional opinion about your problem and will be able to discuss the range of options available.
● Some clinics do not charge for consultations, however, and some use the consultation just to promote their treatments. Make sure you get an independent, professional opinion from a properly trained specialist.

the perfect face

The classic face lift is the most obvious starting point when talking about the face, but there are more options: a less invasive thread lift, or even just the removal of some unsightly veins

FACE LIFT

What is it?

A face lift will restore your youthful features by removing excess skin and fat, and tightening sagging cheeks, deep nasal furrows and down-turning lips. Very few complications occur with a face lift. A face lift will not, however, tackle sagging eyebrows, wrinkles around the mouth, fatty deposits in the eyelids or lines on the forehead.

How it's done

The face lift is usually carried out under general anaesthetic. It is possible to carry out the procedure under local anaesthetic, but the patient would still be advised to stay overnight at the hospital. There are many variations on the 'classic' face lift, but it generally involves a cut being made in the hairline next to the temple, down behind the ear and into the lower hairline. The surgeon then pulls the skin up and trims off any excess fat before closing the wounds with stitches or metal clips on the scalp. A dressing is applied to protect the entire area. With an endoscopic face lift, a tiny fibre-optic camera is inserted through small cuts in the mouth and temple so that the surgeon can see the procedure on a screen. The entire operation can take between 3 and 5 hours.

Healing time

Pain and discomfort lasts for several days while bruising, swelling and numbness may last for a few weeks. Stitches are removed about a week after surgery. You should avoid strenuous activity for at least two weeks after surgery. It may take several months for the full results to be visible.

Is there scarring?

Scarring at the side of the face is permanent.

>>

>> FACE LIFT

However, the operation scars fade over time and are usually hidden by the hair and natural creases of the skin.

HEALING TIME
Bruising and swelling may last a few weeks. Strenuous activity should be avoided for two months.

How long will the effects last?

Results should last between 5 and 10 years. If you are in your forties the effects may last up to 10 years. If you are in your sixties the results may last for 5-7 years.

Is it safe?

Possible complications include infection, reaction to anaesthetic, bleeding, asymmetry and nerve damage, although these are all very rare.

Is it right for me?

The best candidates are those whose skin has retained elasticity and who have a good bone structure. Most women have face lifts between the ages of 40 and 60, although the procedure is also successful for women in their seventies or even in their eighties.

What should I ask?

Could I opt for an alternative type of face lift, such as the S lift or thread lift? Should I be combining this procedure with an endoscopic brow lift to correct the top half of my face? Is there a non-invasive alternative? Should I look into either chemical peels or laser resurfacing to improve wrinkles? How long do you think the results will last for?

FACE LIFT PRICE
£4,000-£8,000

This face lift has rejuvenated her face and removed wrinkles

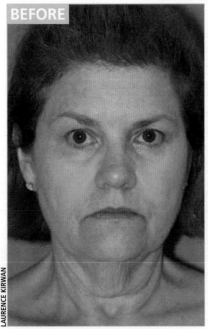
BEFORE

AFTER

LAURENCE KIRWAN

S LIFT SHORT SCAR FACELIFT (MINI FACELIFT)

What is it?

This alternative to the standard face lift rejuvenates the lower part of the face from the temples to the lower neck by lifting facial and neck skin. The layer of tissue connected to the facial muscles is tightened, as are the muscle bands under the skin, effectively elevating the cheek fat to create a more youthful face shape. The name 'S lift' refers to the shape of the scar as it wraps around the ear and lobe and into the hairline for less visible scarring. It involves a shorter scar than the traditional face lift. There tends to be less bruising and the recovery is faster, requiring only about 10 days off work. All stitches can be absorbed and no staples are required.

How it's done

This procedure can be carried out under general or local anaesthetic, although your surgeon will discuss options with you. Incisions begin in the temporal hair area and extend downward in front of the ear, sometimes inside the ear and then behind the ear. Soft tissue structures are tightened and restructured, excess fat and skin are trimmed away and the wounds are closed with fine stitching. Surgery takes 2-3 hours.

Healing time

As the scar is shorter than with a standard face lift, there tends to be less bruising, which means that recovery is faster. The stitches are absorbed by your own body and no staples are required. Your face will feel swollen and stiff at first. Recovery time is around 10 days but it can take around three months for the swelling to disappear completely and the full results to emerge.

Is there scarring?

Usually scarring is minimal, behind and inside the ears or at the hairline.

How long will the effects last?

Results should last 5-10 years depending on how quickly you age. Your surgeon may suggest combining this with an eye lift, chin augmentation or brow lift.

HEALING TIME
The recovery time is around 10 days, though swelling will only fully disappear after three months.

Is it safe?

Possible complications include infection, reaction to anaesthetic and bleeding.

Asymmetry and nerve damage are also possible. Poor surgery can sometimes result in visible scars at the hairline. As with all procedures, it is very important to find a qualified surgeon.

Is it right for me?
Patients of varying ages undergo this procedure, from their thirties and forties, and sometimes into their fifties.

What should I ask?
Should I consider an alternative type of face lift? How often do you carry out this procedure?

'The S lift is not a weekend procedure, but it is ideal for women with a limited amount of time to take out of their hectic business and social schedules'

Laurence Kirwan (MD FRCS) aesthetic plastic surgeon

SPIDER VEIN REMOVAL

What is it?
Spider vein removal is a quick, relatively pain-free laser treatment for the removal of broken veins on the face associated with aging. This treatment is often done in conjunction with other cosmetic surgery procedures like face lifts or eyelid surgery.

How it's done
Intense pulsed light (IPL), light heat energy (LHE) and non-ablative lasers (which work below the top skin layer) are directed at the skin to target blood-filled thread veins. They heat and destroy them without harming the surrounding area. The treatment works quickly and takes only two or three shots of the laser to eliminate the vein. An anaesthetic cream may be applied half an hour before treatment and you will be required to wear eye protectors, but no heavier anaesthetic is used. You may feel a slight tingling when the laser is applied, and the treatment will take 15–30 minutes depending on the size of the area being treated. This usually requires 1-2 treatment sessions.

Healing time
The temporary bruising may last 2-3 weeks and, although the procedure itself may be slightly uncomfortable, no painkillers are required afterwards. Patients should apply aloe vera gel to their face twice a day for a week after treatment.

Is there scarring?
There are no scars with this procedure.

HEALING TIME
Temporary bruising may last three weeks, but you can go about your normal routine as usual.

How long will the effects last?
Facial thread veins may require two treatments, but the results will last up to five years.

Is it safe?
There may occasionally be scabbing and there may be a loss of pigmentation but this is rare. Non-ablative lasers are considered to be safe.

Is it right for me?
Anyone can have this procedure done. There are no age or medical requirements, although you should still have a thorough initial consultation before committing yourself.

What should I ask?
Which type of laser is the most appropriate?

THREAD LIFT

What is it?
A thread lift can have similar effects to that of a full face lift but is less intensive. This procedure is designed to recontour the face by inserting clear threads underneath the skin to add shape and definition, rejuvenating the face in a minimally invasive procedure. Unlike a full face lift, the results are immediately visible, involve no scarring and can be reversed or repeated as you wish.

How it's done
The threads are inserted using a fine needle, after a local anaesthetic has been administered. A surgeon will usually use around 12-16 threads to lift the skin around the brow, mid-face and neck. Your own collagen will surround the threads in order to maintain the elevated effect. The surgery lasts for around two hours.

S LIFT PRICE
£3,000-£4,300

SPIDER VEIN REMOVAL PRICE
£150-£250

>>

>> THREAD LIFT

There are two main types of thread:
● Free-floating threads can either be bi-directional (when the barbs face away or towards each other,) or uni-directional (when the cogs point in the same direction). When the thread is inserted there should be the same number of cogs in each direction in order for the threads to hold position. If inserted incorrectly or not deeply enough, the thread can make its way out of the skin or be visible through the skin. The skin must be pulled into position before the thread is positioned and its ends are cut (below the skin). The threads remain under the skin permanently.
● Suspension/smooth threads are prolene or nylon, absorbable or non-absorbable threads. Because they are attached to a stable structure on the face and scalp, more dramatic results can be achieved. This type of thread is therefore better for women who are seeking a more marked improvement. This procedure is more demanding than the barbed thread procedure and requires a better knowledge of the anatomy, but it produces longer lasting results than the free-floating threads.

Free-floating threads have been known to slip and do not hold the lift as effectively as suspension threads, which need to be attached to a stable structure on the face or scalp. Results of a thread lift using suspension threads are said to be more dramatic than those using free-floating threads.

'The contour threads technique is ideal for the individual who does not need a full face lift but wants to refresh and rejuvenate her looks'

Laurence Kirwan (FRCS) one of the only aesthetic plastic surgeons in Europe qualified to teach this procedure to other surgeons

discomfort, but no serious pain. You'll be able to return to work within a week. The results of a thread lift are immediate.

Is there scarring?
You should expect occasional scarring to occur at needle entry points, but this will fade over time.

How long will the effects last?
The effects will last for about five years and results can be repeated or reversed as you wish.

Is it safe?
Complications can include an adverse reaction to the anaesthetic, haematomas, asymmetry, infection and nerve damage. It is easy to remedy complications with free-floating threads, including puckering or thread protrusion.

Is it right for me?
This procedure is appropriate for 30 to 50 year-olds who require moderate facial rejuvenation.

What should I ask?
Will the thread lift produce the desired results? Which type of thread do you recommend. Do you suggest I combine it with other treatments?

HEALING TIME
here will be bruising and swelling for 24-48 hours. You can return to work after a week.

Healing time
Ice compresses are recommended for the first 24-48 hours to reduce bruising and swelling. You will feel some

TOP TIPS
● Invasive cosmetic surgery should never be entered into lightly.
● Talk to your GP (or another consultant) to get a referral letter before going to the surgeon.
● Your GP will know the specialists in your area and is in the best position to choose the one most appropriate to your needs and your medical history.

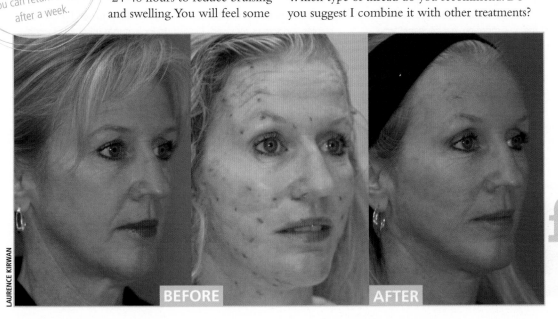

BEFORE

AFTER

LAURENCE KIRWAN

These images show how lines on the face have been minimised and skin is tighter immediately after the thread lift has been performed

£ **THREAD LIFT PRICE**
£1,500+ depending on where the thread lift is carried out

>> FACE LIFT CASE STUDY

Patient:
Debbie Ashcroft, 47, part-time merchandiser
Type of treatment:
endoscopic browlift, neck lift, upper and lower blepharosplasty
Area of treatment: brow, eyes, neck

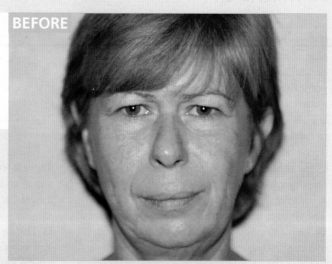

BEFORE

Debbie says she feels much happier since having had her face lift

AFTER

JAN STANEK

Q Why did you choose this particular treatment?
A I got a call inviting me to take part in the new series of Channel Four's *10 Years Younger* programme – it was the answer to my prayers. The 'turkey neck' runs in my family and I applied to the show because I wanted to do something about it.

Q Where did you go for treatment and who administered it?
A The show arranged for me to see Mr Stanek of Surgical Aesthetics. He talked me through the procedures and made me feel very reassured. I thought I was just going to have my neck done but when he pointed out that my brow and eyes could be improved, I couldn't stop looking at them. He held a mirror to my face and manipulated it to show me what could be done. I knew I was never going to get this opportunity again – the procedures would have cost me around £12,000 if I hadn't been on the show.

Q How did you feel before the procedure?
A In the run up to the procedure I was so busy filming for the

programme that I didn't have time to get worried! I had my hair dyed before the operation so that I wouldn't need to do it afterwards when the scars were new, but other than that I didn't really do very much preparation; I just wanted to get it done. I have to admit I didn't sleep very well the night before, but the next day I didn't even have time to stop. The camera crew were filming me, asking how I felt, interviewing Mr Stanek and before I knew it I was on the operating table.

Q How did you feel and look after treatment?
A When I woke up I don't remember feeling much pain but I felt very woozy. I was quite shocked by my appearance and the swelling, but I had been warned what to expect. I looked like I had been in a car accident. I stayed overnight at the hospital and, before leaving the next morning, my bandages were removed and I was given an antibiotic cream to apply around my eyes. I was fine, but I was exhausted. I rested for a few days and at night my husband would give me bags of frozen peas to help keep the swelling down.

Debbie had 64 stitches and all her scars are hidden under her hairline

Q How long did it take to heal?
A The following week I returned to London to have the stitches, staples and screws removed. I was absolutely petrified because I had been unconscious when they had been put in. I had 64 stitches in total and I really didn't like the thought of sitting through having them taken out. Thankfully, the staff were amazing and it didn't hurt either, I think it was just the thought of it. It took a couple of months for the full results to show and I think Mr Stanek did a really good job. At the beginning I could see faint scars beneath my eyes but they quickly faded and I can't see any scars at all now as they are behind my hairline.

Q What impact has the treatment had on your life?
A Having surgery hasn't changed my life; it just means I don't have to look at that miserable face in the mirror any more. No amount of make-up made any difference to the way I looked before.

Q What advice would you have for anyone considering similar surgical procedures?
A I had a great experience, but I wouldn't go out and tell everyone to go out and have surgery. It is a personal decision which everyone has to make for themselves. But, for the ladies who are interested, I would advise them to do their research well and make sure they get a good surgeon.

improved shape

This procedure works by removing fat from certain fatty areas and inserting it into parts of your face that need plumping up, to give you a better defined, younger shape

FAT TRANSFER

What is it?
Fat can be successfully injected into the body to replace fat lost during the aging process, for example in the hollows of the cheeks.

How it's done
This procedure can be carried out under either local or general anaesthetic. Fat is collected from the abdomen, buttocks or thighs by gentle liposuction and the incisions are stitched. The fat is spun, washed and repaired while small incisions are made around the area to be treated, usually the cheeks but also the lips, chin and hollows under the eyes. Tiny needles are used to distribute the fat carefully and evenly in the layer of skin just under the surface. Some discomfort may be felt during fat removal as well as when it is injected into the new area but it is rarely painful. Surgery takes around an hour.

Healing time
You can expect some bruising and swelling at the area where the fat was removed for a few days after the operation, as well as some blood-coloured fluid that will drain from the incisions. The newly injected area may also be swollen and bruised. Patients are advised to keep moving to reduce swelling and prevent blood clots, and to apply cold compresses to help with the swelling. Wearing an elastic garment over the area where the fat was collected from will also help to reduce swelling. You can return to work after 1-7 days.

Is there scarring?
Minor scarring will occur at the incision points but will fade over several months and can be concealed with make-up.

How long will the effects last?
Many doctors will inject too much fat on purpose, as some of it will be reabsorbed into the body. In this case repeat procedures are often required to get a better, more lasting effect which, when finally achieved, can last for many years.

Is it safe?
Possible complications can include infection, reaction to the anaesthetic, numbness and nerve damage in both sites of the body. Patients are advised to contact their surgeon immediately if they notice heavy bleeding, signs of infection or a sudden increase in pain. There is also no risk of allergic reaction as with some other dermal fillers, because the fat comes from your own body.

Is it right for me?
Candidates tend to be in their thirties and over. Most people can have a fat transfer as long as they are in general good health. It can be an advantage for people aiming to lose fat from a particular part of the body.

What should I ask?
Could I use an alternative implant, if filling hollowed out areas, such as the cheeks? Is there a non-invasive alternative? Should I be combining this with another procedure? How many of these procedures have you performed?

HEALING TIME
There will be bruising and swelling for a few days. You can go back to work 1-7 days after surgery.

f **FAT TRANSFER PRICE**
£2,000-£4,000

healthy skin

If you want to make your skin look and feel better, laser resurfacing could be the answer...

LASER RESURFACING

What is it?
Laser resurfacing will reduce lines and wrinkles and improve the appearance and healthiness of skin by targeting the face with intense bursts of energy from a laser. It can be carried out around the mouth, cheeks or face.

How it's done
Ablative (or skin) resurfacing lasers briefly direct an intense burst of laser energy onto the surface of the skin, which heats water within it, causing both water and skin to turn to vapour. Every time the laser is activated, some of the outermost layers of the skin are removed.

HEALING TIME
The surface burn will heal in 3-8 days, and you can expect to return to work after two weeks.

>>

>> LASER RESURFACING

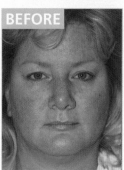

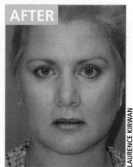

The skin looks much better and is now tighter and firmer

The laser resurfacing procedure lasts from 15-30 minutes for small areas of treatment to over an hour for full face resurfacing. It is performed under local anaesthetic, although this can be combined with mild sedation for larger areas.

Healing time

After treatment, the skin has a raw uncomfortable and weeping surface burn that takes 3-8 days to heal, depending on the extent and depth of the treatment. During this time you will be given a Vaseline-based gel to apply to your skin, and can expect to take two weeks off work. You should wear sunblock on year face for six months. Full results will emerge in around three months.

Is there scarring?

There should be no scarring with this treatment.

How long will the effects last?

The fresher, clearer skin and significant reduction or elimination of lines and wrinkles lasts up to four or five years and can be redone.

Is it safe?

Risks include infection, itching, swelling and pain. Blistering of the skin can occasionally also occur, leading to potential scarring and changes in skin colour, but this is very rare. Infection can be treated with antibiotics and certain pigmentation changes can be treated with products. If you are unhappy with your results, most surgeons are likely to suggest waiting a few months for the face to settle before considering further treatment.

Is it right for me?

Most candidates for this procedure are over 30, wishing to improve the appearance of their skin.

What should I ask?

What type of laser will be used? Is this the best procedure for me?

£ LASER RESURFACING PRICE

£1,600 for a single area of the face, such as eyes or mouth, £2,625 for two areas of the face and from £3,500 for full face treatment

---

lovable lips

From Brigitte Bardot to Angelina Jolie, perfect, luscious lips have a certain allure that little can beat. An implant could make all the difference to you

LIP AUGMENTATION

DID YOU KNOW?

● If you have an operation whose results you're not happy with, a good surgeon will often perform a second operation with no additional surgeon's fee to pay.

● If you feel uncomfortable with your surgeon, he or she can refer you to a colleague for treatment instead.

What is it?

Lips are one of the first areas of the body to age, especially the top lip, which can lose its volume and shape. This quick, fairly simple procedure plumps and reshapes the lips by means of an implant, to help retain a youthful appearance.

How it's done

There are many types of implants, including the synthetic material ePTFE and fat transferred from another part of your own body. Local anaesthetic injections into the lip are all that is usually required to numb the area enough to avoid feeling any pain during the procedure. You may also be given a mild sedative to make you feel drowsy. After making four tiny incisions at

each corner of the mouth, the surgeon will thread strips of the implant through the lip and then stitch the incision areas with either a dissolvable or non-dissolvable thread. The surgery will last for approximately 30 minutes.

Healing time

You should expect to be in some pain after the procedure, especially if you put any pressure around your lips. You may also experience some numbness although this is temporary. Depending on the extent of bruising and swelling after the procedure, you can return to work either the same day or 2-3 days afterwards. During the healing stage, which can last for several weeks, lip implants can feel stiff, making eating and drinking difficult.

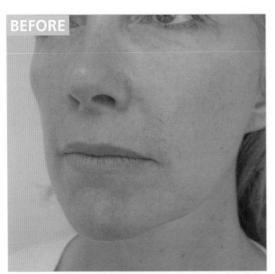

BEFORE

Her lips are far fuller after the lip augmentation

AFTER

LUCY GLANCEY

inserted. The positioning and shape of teeth may also affect the appearance of the lips after surgery.

Is it safe?
Possible complications include infection, numbness and nerve damage, although these complications are all quite rare. The other risk is that the implant might move or that scar tissue may develop around it, in which case further surgery will be necessary.

Is it right for me?
Anyone can undergo this procedure. You should talk it over with your consultant to find out if it will achieve the desired results.

What should I ask?
What type of implant do you recommend?

£ LIP AUGMENTATION PRICE
£1,000-£2,000 depending on the type of implant used

graceful neck

A neck lift will tighten your muscles and banish any sagging skin, making you feel like a new person

NECK LIFT (PLATYMAPLASTY)

What is it?
Neck lifts are usually performed as part of a face lift. The neck lift removes sagging skin in the neck area and under the jaw line, tightening muscles to create a more youthful appearance. Liposuction can also be performed at the same time to remove a double chin.

How it's done
Most neck lift procedures are performed under a general anaesthetic. Incisions are made under the chin and behind or under the ear so that the surgeon can tighten muscles and skin and firm up the appearance of the neck. If the patient has excessive amounts of fat in the chin area as well, the surgeon may use liposuction to reduce it. Excess skin is trimmed away before the wound is closed with stitches or tissue glue, usually behind or below the ear. A pressure dressing is then placed around the head to help the wound heal.

Healing time
Pain, swelling and stiffness should be expected and any stitches won't be removed for around a week. You may notice a change in your smile.

HEALING TIME
Lips will take several weeks to heal fully, but you can return to work on the same day if you want.

Your surgeon may recommend applying arnica to help reduce the bruising and speed up your recovery. Most complications, such as excessive swelling, settle within three months, but if the implant hardens or shifts it may need replacing.

Is there scarring?
Minor scarring will occur at the incision points but will fade over time and can be easily concealed with make-up.

How long will the effects last?
If the implants are synthetic, like ePTFE for example, their effect will be permanent. If you choose a non-permanent implant material, however, you will need to return to your surgeon every six months or so to have another implant

BEFORE

Loose neck skin is removed

AFTER

THE POUNTNEY CLINIC

>>

>> NECK LIFT

You may also feel burning, tingling and sporadic sharp pain. You are advised to rest for up to three weeks, taking care not to bend over or lift heavy objects. Many symptoms will subside in a few weeks but it may take several months for the swelling to subside.

Is there scarring?
There is a risk of scarring although scars may be hidden in the folds of the skin and behind the ear. If any scarring does occur, it can take up to two years to fade.

How long will the effects last?
The results last for 5–10 years, depending on the age you are when you have the surgery and how

well you age. The older you get, the faster your cells degenerate and the shorter the effects last.

Is it safe?
There is the possibility of a reaction to anaesthesia, infection, numbness, bleeding, asymmetry, lumpiness and mottling of the skin. Puckering of the skin may occur and excessive scar tissue is possible too, although this is rare.

What should I ask?
Should I combine the neck lift with a chin tuck to remove excess fat? Do you also recommend a face lift? Are there any other procedures I should be thinking about?

Is it right for me?
Patients who decide to have this procedure done are usually over 40.

HEALING TIME
You must rest for three weeks after the operation. It may take several months for final results to show.

£
NECK LIFT PRICE
£3,500-£4,000

delicate nose

If you're not happy with the size or shape of your nose, you're not alone. Rhinoplasty is one of the most popular cosmetic surgery procedures

NOSE JOB (RHINOPLASTY)

What is it?
The size and shape of your nose is one of the most defining characteristics of your face, affecting your profile as well as the overall feel of your face. If you are unhappy with your nose, this can affect every aspect of your self-perception, and a nose job (more formally known as rhinoplasty) can dramatically alter your whole appearance, creating a more balanced or symmetrical look. This procedure makes it possible to reshape the nose, increase or reduce its size, straighten a lump on

the bridge, narrow the nostrils, change the shape of the tip or change the angle between the nose and upper lip.

How it's done
Rhinoplasty can be carried out under general or local anaesthesic, depending on the extent of the procedure and your surgeon's recommendation. The operation is performed either through an open or closed approach.
● With the closed procedure, the skin is cut inside the rim of the nostrils to avoid visible scarring.
● In the open procedure, which enables the surgeon to have a clearer view of the cartilage in the tip of the nose, an incision is made across the base of the nose, which can leave a small scar on the area between the nostrils.

During surgery, the soft tissue of the nose is separated from the bone and cartilage under the skin. The bone may be broken and the cartilage reshaped or chiselled to create the desired look. The bones on the side of the nose can be moved inward to allow for a narrower bridge.

'Sometimes patients fail to transmit their true expectations, asking for an average-shaped nose whereas, in fact, they really wanted a marked ski slope shape. Make sure that both you and the surgeon have discussed what you wish to see and whether it is possible in your case'

Lucian Ion cosmetic surgeon

After surgery, a splint is applied and the nostrils are lightly packed with medicated gauze. Stitches are used to close internal wounds and will dissolve automatically, but stitches used on the skin separating the nostrils may need to be removed.

Time to heal
The operation is usually associated with a dull ache rather than pain, and the main swelling and bruising settle down after two weeks. If the nasal bone is broken in the procedure it is normal to expect blackening around the eyes. The cast on the bridge of the nose is removed after one week and, at the same time, the stitches on the underside of the nose are removed. It will already be possible to see considerable changes after two weeks, but the swelling affecting the bridge and the tip of the nose can take several months to settle down properly. It is important to be patient as your appearance will change significantly during the first three months and it can take 1–2 years to see the final results.

Is there scarring?
With a simple, closed rhinoplasty procedure there will not be any visible scars, as the scarring occurs only on the inside of the nose. With an open tip approach, there will be a small scar on the area between the nostrils called the columella. This small scar fades after two months, becoming very difficult to see. It can also be covered with make-up in the meantime.

How long will the effects last?
It is important to have realistic expectations about the results of this procedure. It won't be possible to pick your ideal nose out from a magazine: the surgeon can only work with your existing nose. But this procedure can be very successful and the results will last a lifetime. Repeat surgery is possible if you are not happy with the outcome, but you usually have to wait between 6 and 12 months after the first operation.

Is it safe?
Apart from the relatively low risk of reacting badly to the anaesthetic, it is possible that the definition at the tip or the shape of the bridge may not be as good as expected. Possible side effects include headaches and nasal

HEALING TIME
Most of the bruising will go after two weeks, but swelling may take several months to calm down.

BEFORE

AFTER

LUCIAN ION

The results of a rhinoplasty procedure can be dramatic

bleeding. Risks associated with surgery include infection, reactions to anaesthesia, nerve damage, haematomas and irregularities such as a lop-sided nose. Repeat surgery is possible but should not be rushed into.

£ **RHINOPLASTY PRICE**
£2,000–£3,500

Is it right for me?
The rhinoplasty procedure can be carried out any time after the nose has fully developed at 18.

What should I ask?
How many rhinoplasty procedures do you carry out? What is your complication rate? What is your insurance policy if something goes wrong?

WHAT THE SURGEONS SAY
"Women are focusing on their careers for longer, starting families later and remaining active well into their sixties and seventies. They want their faces to reflect this."
Angelica Kouvani (MD, FRCS), Cosmetic Solution

"It's like decorating a home: if you put the wallpaper up but don't paint the rim you don't get the results."
Laurence Kirwan (MD, FRCS), Harley Street

"You need to like a surgeon and you need to go by reputation."
Jan Stanek (FRCS), Surgical Aesthetics

"If you feel uneasy then go and see somebody else, because it probably isn't right."
Dai Davies (FRCS), Plastic Surgery Partners

5

the body
COSMETIC SURGERY

There's no doubt about it, having an invasive cosmetic surgery procedure is a big decision. But there's no need to be scared off by the horror stories that used to appear in the newspapers. Since the late 1980s, cosmetic surgeons have carefully studied skin and fat structure and how our shape changes as we age, enabling them to adapt their surgery to perform operations with more consistent results and fewer complications. It is true that all surgery does come with risks, but there are also great benefits to undergoing a cosmetic procedure. The guidelines that follow should enable you to make an informed decision about which treatment is right for you.

In 2004, BAAPS (British Association of Aesthetic Plastic Surgeons) members conducted 15,019 invasive cosmetic procedures on women – a 60% increase on 2003

Body sculpting

COSMETIC SURGERY FOR THE BODY

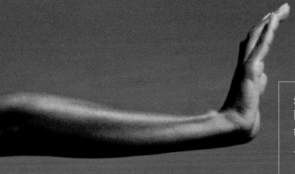

I N RECENT YEARS, ADVANCES IN SURGERY
have brought about operations to deal with our every flaw
and imperfection. From traditional breast lifts to belly button
surgery, doctors are developing new ways to make surgery
better, safer and longer-lasting. And it seems we are trusting
these operations more and more: in 2004, BAAPS (British
Association of Aesthetic Plastic Surgeons) members conducted
15,019 invasive cosmetic procedures on women – a 60%
increase on 2003.

Before diving in, make sure you are fully informed. All
invasive procedures are intricate surgical operations that should
only be performed by highly skilled and experienced cosmetic
surgeons. As such, your first rule of thumb is to always have
consultations with two or more surgeons. Obtain as much
information as necessary to make a fully informed choice and
make sure you get satisfactory answers to all your questions.

Always set out your expectations and the results you desire
in your first consultation with a surgeon. However, you must be
realistic: the results of cosmetic surgery are usually subtle and
designed to achieve better harmony of bodily features, not turn
you into Kate Moss! Patients who look forward to a miraculous
transformation are inevitably disappointed. Also bear in mind
that results vary enormously depending upon both the patient
and the individual surgeon, so outcomes for cosmetic surgery
procedures will always be quite variable.

There are few reasons why you should not undergo surgery as
long as you are in good general health. With all operations, if
you start out in good physical condition, recovery will be faster.

It is highly unlikely that anyone considering these procedures
would be able to access them free of charge on the National
Health Service. However, there are special cases, and it is
recommended that you visit your GP before embarking upon a
cosmetic procedure involving surgery.

If you are considering invasive cosmetic surgery for the body,
the following information will give you a basic understanding
of the procedures available.Now read on and find out the
possibilities for a new, younger you...

DID YOU KNOW?

For all procedures, a
medical history should
be taken. You will
normally be asked to
sign a consent form,
which means you
have understood the
potential benefits and
risks associated with
the procedure. The
surgeon may write to
your GP giving details
of the operation,
and photographs
may be taken by the
practitioner so you
can have a 'before
and after' comparison
at a later date.

GOODSHOOT

firmer arms

BEFORE

Sagging skin is removed

AFTER

LAURENCE KIRWAN

It's easy to think of tummy tucks and boob jobs as the main cosmetic procedures, but there are lots of others. If you have severely flabby upper arms, for example, an arm lift could help to solve the problem

ARM LIFT (BRACHIOPLASTY)

ARM LIFT PRICE
From £3,000 for both arms, £4,000 with liposuction

What is it?
An arm lift is a body contouring procedure that is designed to remove excess skin and fat from the upper arm area, giving a firmer, tighter, more youthful appearance.

How it's done
Upper arm lifts are usually performed under a general anaesthetic. The surgeon will make long cuts through the underneath of the upper arm in a crescent shape. The excess segments of skin and fat are then removed from the upper arm, and the remaining skin and tissue are lifted to achieve a tighter and smoother effect. An upper arm lift will usually take around 2 hours, depending on the extent of work required, and whether any other procedures such as liposuction are also involved to remove large amounts of fat. This additional liposuction may be necessary for arms bearing an excessive amount of fat

Time to heal
Arms will be bruised and swollen immediately after surgery, with swelling taking up to three months to disappear completely. Numbness of the skin around the upper arms is common and it may take several months for the sensation to return. Most patients are able to leave hospital after a day or so and return to work within 1-2 weeks. Vigorous exercise can be resumed after approximately 4-6 weeks.

Is there scarring?
Yes. Scarring is permanent. Scars will run down from the armpit to the elbow on the inner side of the arm, and will be curved to help them heal as quickly as possible. Scars may appear to get worse during the first 3-6 months but they will flatten out and lighten in colour within 9-12 months. The length of the scar will depend on how much excess skin is removed.

GOOD FOR?
☑ upper arms with flabby or sagging skin

How long will the effects last?
The effects of the surgery are permanent, as long as there is not any excessive weight gain following the procedure. Liposuction can also be performed alongside an upper arm lift to improve the final result, but how long the effects last will ultimately be decided by your own diet after the surgery.

Is it safe?
Possible complications can include infection, reaction to the anaesthetic, blood or fluid collection underneath the skin, nerve damage, blood clots, and an irregular or a 'lop-sided' appearance of the arms after the operation; however, these are all quite rare.

What should I ask?
Could I achieve the same effect with liposuction alone? Will I also need liposuction to complement the procedure?

Is it right for me?
This is right for people who have lost skin elasticity due to ageing or weight loss, and now have visible saggy skin around the upper arm area.

Contraindications
This surgery is not suitable after a mastectomy (breast removal), an operation in the axilla lymph nodes or for those prone to infections of the sweat glands, as these may cause problems with draining fluids from the arms following surgery.

'After an arm lift procedure, a patient will be out of action for around two weeks. Scars tend to be quite visible and red for six months, but should fade after a year. As it is quite an extensive procedure, I would only recommend it for those who have experienced heavy weight loss or have what is known as a 'bat arm' deformity '

Erik Scholten, Hurlingham Clinic

beautiful breasts

Feeling underconfident about your breasts, whether you think they're too big or too small, can have an enormous impact on your own sense of self. Breast surgery could give you the shape you've always longed for

BREAST ENLARGEMENT

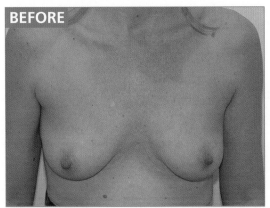

BEFORE

Breasts are fuller after the augmentation procedure

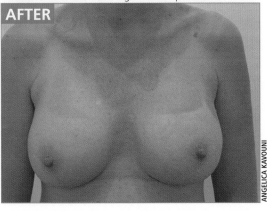

AFTER

ANGELICA KAVOUNI

GOOD FOR?

☑ women who are unhappy with their breast size and shape

☑ those wishing to regain breast size or shape after childbirth

☑ women with a deformity on one or both breasts

Time to heal

You can often go home on the day of surgery and find that you can return to work after a few days' recuperation. You should allow 14–21 days for recovery. You will feel sore and tired and may experience a burning sensation in the nipples for some days after the operation, which will ease as the bruising starts to go down. Swelling can take 3-5 weeks to go completely.

Is there scarring?

Scars will be small and may be pink for several weeks. They will begin to fade after a few months, although the scarring will never disappear completely. Depending on the type of incision, they may be underneath the breast, around the nipple or in the armpit.

How long will the effects last?

The operation usually needs repeating every 10-16 years, so be prepared for the possibility of repeat procedures.

Is it safe?

Possible complications can include infection, bleeding, asymmetry between breasts, poor positioning, silicone leakage or scar contracture. If you develop an infection, or the silicone leaks or the scar tissue contracts, the implant will deform.

What is it?

There are many different types of breast enlargement but, essentially, the surgery will involve inserting an implant into the breast to make it bigger and give it a fuller shape.

How it's done

The surgeon will advise you on which shape of implant and method of inserting it will be right for you. The surgery itself involves a short incision that can be made either in the crease under the breast, around the areola (the dark skin around the nipple) or in the armpit. Implants may then be positioned either between the glandular tissue of the breast and the pectoral muscle (sub-glandular) or behind the muscle (sub-muscular). Slow dissolving stitches are used to sew up the wounds. Surgery takes around 90 minutes.

£ **BREAST ENLARGEMENT PRICE**
£3,000-£5,000 for both breasts, depending on the surgeon and the type of implant

'There is quite a lot of swelling and bruising initially with a breast augmentation. However, this does settle down over 4-6 weeks and patients will be able to see the improved size and shape of their breast. Within two months of surgery there is no visible sign that surgery has been done'

Angelica Kavouni, Cosmetic Solutions

>>

>> BREAST ENLARGEMENT

This is known as capsular contracture and, in this case, the implant will have to be removed. You may experience less nipple sensation after breast enhancement, and in a minority of cases this can be a permanent state. There is no evidence that breast implants affect fertility, pregnancy, or the ability to breastfeed a baby.

What should I ask?

Should I have a smooth or textured implant? Should I have a saline or silicone implant? Should I have a round or teardrop shape? Will I also need a breast lift to achieve the desired effect? How big should the implants be? What are the pros and cons of the different incisions/implants?

Is it right for me?

The best candidates for this surgery tend to be in their twenties or thirties.

Contraindications

If you are prone to red, angry, raised scars, your surgeon may caution you that the scars from this procedure could be very visible.

TYPES OF IMPLANTS

There are two main filler types in the UK:
● A silicone implant is semi-liquid and moves easily so that it can maintain a good shape and give a more natural feel.
● A saline implant is placed inside the breast then filled with salt water. This reduces the size of the cut required and leaves a smaller scar.
● Rupture used to be common with early thin-walled silicone implants, but this is now less frequent due to medical advances.

£ BREAST LIFT PRICE

£3,000 for a breast lift, up to £5,500+ if implants are included

---

BREAST LIFT (MASTOPLEXY)

What is it?

A breast lift raises the breast tissue, repositions the nipple and enhances breast shape, leaving it looking more pert – it does not increase the size of the breast. Women who undergo a breast lift may also seek to increase the size of their breasts with a breast implant, as a breast augmentation is the only way to increase breast firmness and size.

The operation

There are different techniques that can be used for a breast lift. The 'anchor' method involves one cut underneath the breast, following the breast's natural curve, and a cut that runs from the nipple to the bottom of the breast. When the excess skin has been removed, the nipple is moved up and the skin around it is pulled tightly down to reshape the breast. Stitches are put in around the nipple, in a line running down the lower crease of the breast.

For those with smaller breasts which have lost their perkiness, the 'doughnut' procedure is used, involving one circular cut around the areola, and a doughnut-shaped area of skin being removed. This requires fewer incisions, which minimises the scarring. A breast lift takes 1.5–3.5 hours.

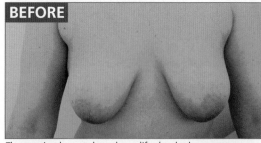
BEFORE

The sagging breasts have been lifted to look more pert

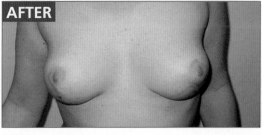
AFTER

ANGELICA KAVOUNI

Time to heal

Some patients may be up and about in a day or two, but you shouldn't plan on returning to work for around 1-2 weeks. Breasts will be tender, bruised and swollen after this operation and swelling can occasionally last for many weeks. A support bra must to be worn around the clock for 3-4 weeks after surgery and stitches will need to be removed after a week or two.

Is there scarring?

Recently, surgeons have been trying to reduce the number of visible scars used in the surgery without reducing the effectiveness of the operation. However, a breast lift does leave noticeable, permanent scars.

'The uplift is ideal for people who have lost a lot of weight or breastfed children. The excess skin is removed and the breast is tightened to become more firm and round. My clients are always pleased with the results'

Angelica Kavouni, Cosmetic Solutions

GOOD FOR?
☑ misshapen, saggy breasts
☑ breasts that lack firmness
☑ nipples that have stretched over time

They often remain lumpy and red for months, and then gradually become less obvious, sometimes eventually fading to thin white lines. Poor healing and wider scars are more common in smokers.

How long will the effects last?

A breast lift will not make your breasts firm forever. The natural effects of gravity, pregnancy, ageing and weight fluctuations will eventually take their toll again and your breasts may alter in shape and firmness. Women who have breast implants at the same time as a breast lift may find the results last longer.

Is it safe?

Possible complications include infection, a reaction to the anaesthesia, bleeding and nerve damage. The procedure can also leave you with unevenly positioned nipples, or a permanent loss of feeling in your nipples or breasts. The operation should not affect your ability to breastfeed, since milk ducts and nipples will not be interfered with by the surgery.

What should I ask?

Will the operation affect my ability to breastfeed? Should I wait until after I've had children? Will I also need to have a breast implant to achieve the desired effect?

Is it right for me?

This procedure fixes sagging breast tissue, so is ideal for women whose breasts have lost their shape and tone due to age, weight loss or childbirth. The best results are usually achieved in women with small, sagging breasts. Breasts of any size can be lifted, but the results may not last as long in heavy breasts.

Contraindications

If you're planning to have more children, it may be a good idea to postpone your breast lift until you have completed your family.

DID YOU KNOW?

A new method of temporary breast enhancement through fat injection is currently undergoing pilot studies in the US. This filler, developed by Q-med, is called Macrolane and is made from hyaluronic acid (the same product used in some facial fillers). It would be injected into the breast tissue to give a breast boost lasting approximately two years.

BREAST REDUCTION
(REDUCTION MAMMAPLASTY)

What is it?

This procedure removes fat, tissue and skin from the breasts to reduce and reshape them, removing the physical discomfort of large breasts and making the body look better proportioned. Your breasts will have a more youthful shape and be much lighter and higher.

How it's done

The most common breast reduction technique is the 'anchor' method, which involves cutting around the areola, down the breast and then underneath the natural crease beneath the breast. Excess tissue and skin are removed, then the nipple and areola are placed in a new, higher position. Skin from the sides of the breast is pulled down and around the areola, making the new smaller, tighter, firmer shape of the breast.

GOOD FOR?
☑ large, heavy and oversized breasts

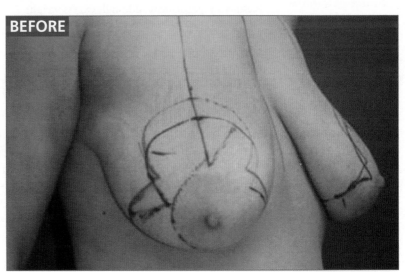

BEFORE

The breast reduction removes excess skin and tissue and repositions the nipple

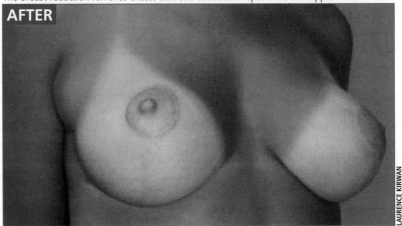

AFTER

LAURENCE KIRWAN

>>

>> BREAST REDUCTION

Any excess fat can be removed with liposuction in the armpit area. A tube is put into the armpit and the fat is simply sucked out through it. The procedure would normally take 2-4 hours.

Time to heal

Recovery can take up to two weeks. Breasts will be tender and bruised, with swelling potentially lasting several weeks. A soft support bra will need to be worn for 3-4 weeks, and stitches will need to be removed after 1-2 weeks.

Is there scarring?

Scarring is more prominent with breast reduction than with breast augmentation. The scars will be noticeable and permanent, and may remain lumpy and red for several months, gradually becoming less obvious and fading to thin white lines. Poor healing and wider scars tend to be more common in smokers.

How long will the effects last?

Results are permanent, although excess weight gain may cause the breasts to grow.

Is it safe?

Possible complications include loss of nipple sensation, lopsided nipples, infection, a reaction to the anaesthetic, bleeding, nerve damage and an inability to breastfeed afterwards.

What should I ask?

Where will the nipple and areola be positioned? Where will the scars be? Could liposuction alone achieve the same results in reducing breast size, without such noticeable scarring?

Is it right for me?

The ideal candidates are women over 20 with fully developed large breasts that are uncomfortable and cause them pain in their shoulders, back or neck, preventing daily activities including exercise.

Contraindications

If you are prone to keloid (red, angry, raised) scars, your surgeon may not recommend this procedure or may caution you that scars could be raised and very visible.

£
BREAST REDUCTION PRICE
From £3,000, but up to £7,500 if liposuction is also required to remove excess fat

>> BREAST REDUCTION CASE STUDY

Patient: Lucy Alder, 34, advertising executive
Type of treatment: breast reduction and liposuction

Q Why did you choose to have this procedure?
A I've had a big chest since the age of 13 and have always hated them. I am a G cup and the weight of my breasts has caused muscle damage in the back of my neck and shoulders. Shopping was a nightmare as I was a size 18 on the top and a 12 on the bottom. I decided that the only way to make myself feel happier and healthier was to have surgery.

Q Where did you go for surgery?
A I went to Dr Kirwan at his surgery in London as he had been recommended by my mother-in-law, but I made sure I had a consultation with another surgeon

too, as it's always good to get a second opinion.

Q How much did it cost?
A I saved up for 5 years to raise the £6,800 for the procedure with Dr Kirwan.

Q How did you feel during and after surgery?
A I was a bit nervous before surgery and afterwards I was in a lot of pain – for two days I was on morphine and it felt like an elephant was sitting on my chest! However, when the bandages came off and I saw the results I knew it was worth it. Now I am a D cup and I only have small, faint scars that run around my nipple and from my nipple to the

bottom of the breast in an anchor shape. The reduction operation was combined with liposuction under my arms and down the side of my ribcage to ensure I looked in proportion, and I had a slight lift to prevent sagging.

Q Did you suffer any negative side effects?
A Well, I had to take six weeks off work. I was in bed for the first week and couldn't drive or lift my arms for the first month but after that the pain subsided and it got much easier.

Q What impact has the treatment had on your life?
A Now I am so much more confident. I can wear what I like and don't even have to wear a bra. I can walk straight, go to exercise classes and don't need

the physio sessions I was having before to sort out my aching neck and shoulders. I'm a new person.

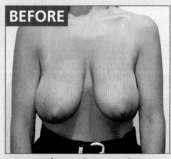
BEFORE
Lucy went from a G cup to a D cup

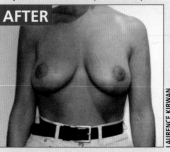
AFTER

LAURENCE KIRWAN

buttock lift

Some of us spend time worrying that our bums are too big, but a popular surgical procedure is buttock augmentation, where flat or drooping buttocks are lifted or given implants to give a firm, smooth shape

BUTTOCK AUGMENTATION/IMPLANTS

GOOD FOR?
☑ flat, unrounded buttocks
☑ excessively fatty and flabby buttocks
☑ misshapen buttocks

What is it?

Buttocks begin to droop and change shape as we grow older, so a buttock lift or implants are designed to tighten and lift the buttocks, making the bottom rounder, firmer and smoother. For patients with good skin quality and tone, whose buttocks are flat rather than rounded, buttock implants may be recommended to help produce a more rounded shape to the bottom. For patients with excess fat around the sides of the buttocks who, again, have good skin quality and tone, liposuction alone provides the best results in helping to reshape the buttocks. In such cases, the excess fat can simply be sucked out, rather than having a lift.

How it's done

Buttock lifts are usually performed under a general anaesthetic. Half moon-shaped segments of skin and fat are removed from the buttock area, then the remaining skin and tissue is lifted to achieve a tighter and smoother effect. If there is a large excess of fat, the buttock augmentation can be complemented with liposuction. The procedure takes several hours, depending on how much work is required, and whether any liposuction is involved.

For buttock implants, a 2-3 inch incision is made between the buttocks overlying the tailbone, then the buttock muscle is lifted up and a pocket is made just large enough for the implant to be inserted. Both sides are carefully examined in order to assure that the results look natural and symmetrical. The incisions are then closed with fine, dissolving stitches. The procedure usually takes 1.5 hours to complete using a general anaesthetic and normally includes an overnight stay in hospital.

Time to heal

Bruising after the surgery is usually quite light but swelling is considerable and can take 3-4 months to disappear. You may also experience numbness of the skin around the buttocks and it may take several months for the sensation to return. A support garment will need to be worn for 3-4 weeks to help with the reshaping, especially if liposuction was performed.

Is there scarring?

The length of the scar will depend on how much excess skin you have. Typically, the scar will stretch from hip to hip across your buttocks but will be usually be hidden by your underwear. The scars may actually appear to worsen during the first 3-6 months as they heal, but this is normal. They will flatten out and become lighter in colour within 9-12 months.

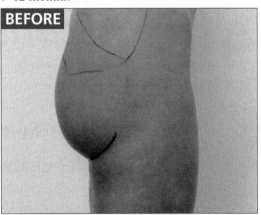

BEFORE

The buttocks have an improved shape after the procedure

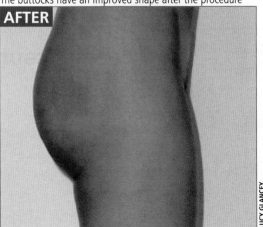

AFTER

LUCY GLANCEY

DID YOU KNOW?

● Many cultures all over the world have valued large buttocks, from primitive Africa to modern Europe.

● The larger posterior has been made popular again recently by singers like Jennifer Lopez and Beyonce appearing in the media.

● The number of buttock augmentation procedures performed in the US increased by a staggering 533% in 2003.

>>

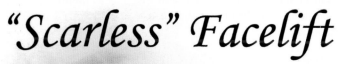

>> BUTTOCK AUGMENTATION/IMPLANTS

How long will the effects last?
The results of the procedure should be permanent providing that you follow the cosmetic surgeon's advice and do not gain a large amount of weight after the operation.

Is it safe?
Possible complications with any surgery can include infection, a reaction to the anaesthetic, blood or fluid collection underneath the skin, nerve damage and blood clots. An irregular or a lopsided appearance of the buttocks is also possible with this procedure, although all of these complications are very rare in the hands of an experienced surgeon.

What should I ask?
Will I need liposuction as well as a lift? What is the difference between a lift and an implant? Which one is right for me? Would a synthetic implant or a fat injection be better?

Is it right for me?
Ideal candidates are those who have large amounts of loose or sagging skin around the buttocks, or who would like their bottom reshaped to be rounder and firmer.

Contraindications
Patients who have had phlebitis (inflamed blood vessels) in their legs may not be suitable.

£ BUTTOCK AUGMENTATION / IMPLANTS PRICE
£5,000-£6,500 for a lift; £3,000-£4,000 for implants. Prices will vary depending on the surgeon. You should expect to pay an extra £1,000 if liposuction is also required

stunning thighs

It's easy to overlook the thighs, as they're usually obscured by clothing. When it's time to hit the beach though, we're reminded of their presence, and wonder what it might be like to look a little different...

THIGH LIFT

What is it?
A thigh lift (sometimes known as a 'thighplasty') is a body contouring procedure designed to remove large amounts of skin and fat from the hips and thighs. It can dramatically improve the appearance of sagging thighs.

How it's done
Thigh lifts are usually performed under a general anaesthetic. Elliptical segments of skin and fat are removed from the thigh area, then the remaining skin and tissue are lifted to achieve a tightening and smoothing effect. The procedure takes 2-3 hours, depending on the extent of the work required, and whether any combined procedures are involved, such as liposuction.

Time to heal
The thigh lift procedure has a prolonged recovery time. There is a significant amount of pain and discomfort during the healing process. Bruising is evident and can spread down the legs. Swelling can be substantial and takes up to 3-4 months to disappear. You may also experience numbness of the skin around the thighs and it could take

several months for the sensation to return fully. Some form of support garment will need to be worn for 3-4 weeks after surgery.

Is there scarring?
This operation involves long cuts and, inevitably, long scars. Scars extend across the outer and inner thighs. Wherever possible, these are positioned so that they can be hidden within a bikini line. Scars may actually appear to worsen during the first 3-6 months as they heal, but will flatten out and lighten in colour within 9-12 months.

How long will the effects last?
Longevity depends upon maintaining weight control, as excessive weight gain after the procedure will cause the tightened skin to stretch.

Is it safe?
Possible complications include infection, a reaction to the anaesthesia, blood or fluid collection underneath the skin, nerve damage or blood clots. The superficial lymphatic system in the groin (which is a part of the immune system) is occasionally interrupted during the thigh lift.

GOOD FOR?
☑ sagging or flabby thighs with excess skin or fat

>>

>> THIGH LIFT

THIGH LIFT PRICE
£5,000-£6,000 for both legs, plus £1,000 if liposuction is required

This can causing severe swelling which will fade within 4-6 weeks.

What should I ask?
Could liposuction achieve the same result? Will I need a more extensive operation such as a lower body lift to achieve the desired effect? Should I combine this procedure with liposuction or a buttock lift to enhance the result? Should I consider calf implants to make my legs more shapely/in proportion?

Is it right for me?
The ideal candidate for this procedure is someone with very saggy skin around the thigh and hip area, as a result of poor skin tone related to the normal aging process, multiple pregnancies or significant weight loss.

Contraindications
If you have had phlebitis (inflamed blood vessels) in either of your legs, you may not be a candidate for lift surgery. As this is not a common procedure in the UK, it may be difficult to find someone who specialises in this procedure.

'The thigh lift is a tricky procedure – at present I only perform two or three per year. However, it is becoming more prevalent as we see more patients with massive weight loss. They are always incredibly pleased with the results, they experience less sweatiness and chafing, making walking around so much easier'

Erik Scholten, Hurlingham Clinic

the lower body

There are lots of different ways to improve your lower body area, from perfecting your belly button to reducing fatty bulges with liposuction, to going all the way and deciding to have a tummy tuck

BELLY BUTTON ENHANCEMENT
(UMBILICOPLASTY)

GOOD FOR?
☑ outward facing belly button
☑ oversized belly button hole
☑ hernias that stick out next to the belly button

What is it
This procedure turns an outward facing belly button into an inward facing one. It can also sometimes be used to remove hernias, which may stick out in a little lump next to the belly button.

How it's done
It can be performed using local anaesthetic to numb the area around the belly button. It is combined with a sedative so that patients remain awake but drowsy. Different techniques are used to reshape the belly button depending on the surgeon and the type of new shape required. The surgeon usually cuts the skin inside the belly button to reshape it, stitching with dissolvable stitches that do not need to be removed. Surgery usually takes an hour, but can be longer if an umbilical hernia needs to be repaired or removed.

Time to heal
Most patients are released from hospital after a few hours and are able to return to light activities the day after the operation. Full recovery generally takes a week or so.

Is there scarring?
The scarring is usually hidden as the surgeon tries to cut the skin inside the belly button.

How long will the effects last?
The surgery is usually permanent, providing patients do not lose or gain too much weight.

Is it safe?
This is one of the lower risk cosmetic surgery procedures available: pain, bruising and swelling are usually quite mild. Rare complications include infection, a reaction to anaesthesia, blood or fluid collection underneath the skin, numbness and an irregular appearance of the belly button, which may require further surgery to correct.

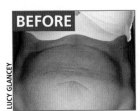 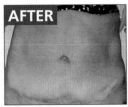

The belly button has been given definition by the surgery

What should I ask?
Will I need a tummy tuck to achieve the desired effect? Should I lose weight prior to the procedure? Are there other procedures I should be having done at the same time?

Is it right for me?
The best candidates are those with no belly button at all, or one that is hidden by folds of flesh or wrinkles. It is also best for those with a misshapen or non-central navel, or who wish to have a flat or elongated navel made rounder.

Contraindications
This procedure is not recommended if you are pregnant or planning on having a child in the near future.

BODY SCULPTING (USING PUAL)

What is it?
PUAL (pulse ultrasound-assisted lipoplasty) is a liposuction procedure used in areas of the body where fat is much tougher to break down. It is a precise technique so works well in areas such as the legs, abdomen or buttocks, as well as smaller areas like the chin and neck. Patients will see smoothed contouring in treated areas. PUAL is also known as the Vaser system.

How it's done
The anaesthetic may be local or general depending on your surgeon's recommendation. PUAL uses a special cannula (a hollow suction tube) to produce short bursts of ultrasonic sound waves. These energy waves break down the walls of the fat cells, turning fat into liquid so it can be easily removed and taking as little as 20 minutes. Some pressure, movement and stinging can be felt while fat is removed, but it is rarely painful.

Time to heal
Although a small incision is made (around 3mm), PUAL allows the quick removal of tissue with far less bruising and tenderness than traditional liposuction, so healing is 30% quicker than with older procedures. Bruising, swelling, and some blood-coloured fluid leaking from the wounds can be expected for a few days. Depending on the extent of the procedure, most patients return to work within a few days to a week.

Is there scarring?
There can potentially be skin discolouration or scarring at the incision points.

How long will the effects last?
Results achieved with this procedure can be permanent as long as patients exercise and have a sensible diet. Some patients may require a repeat procedure in the future in order to achieve or maintain the desired result.

Is it safe?
Problems which can occur during surgery include infection, numbness, nerve damage, unevenness, persistent swelling, as well as lumpiness at the site of the liposuction. With ultrasound, there may also be a risk of burns to the outer layers and deeper tissues under the skin. Although occurring very rarely, more serious complications can include blood clots and severe infections.

What should I ask?
Would PUAL or liposuction be more appropriate for the result that I want? What lifestyle changes will I need to make after the operation?

GOOD FOR?
- ☑ effective on legs, abdomen, buttocks and hips
- ☑ areas where fat is difficult to break down, such as on the back and arms
- ☑ small, fatty areas, such as the neck and chin

£ BODY SCULPTING PRICE
From £850 for one small area to £5,000 for a large area with a great deal of fat to be removed

The area treated with PUAL is smoother and firmer

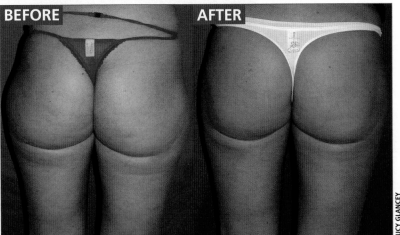

>>

£ BODY SCULPTING PRICE

£850-£5,000 depending on the areas being treated

>> BODY SCULPTING

How much fat can be removed? Will repeat treatments be necessary?

Is it right for me?

This is good for over 30s with stubborn fat.

Contraindications

A tummy tuck may be more appropriate for patients with an excess of sagging skin.

LIPOSUCTION

GOOD FOR?

☑ thighs and hips
☑ waist
☑ buttocks
☑ arms
☑ chin
☑ knees and ankles

What is it?

Liposuction (also known as liposculpture, or suction-assisted lipectomy) is good for reducing fatty bulges from many areas of the body, from hips and thighs to the chin or ankles. It is frequently performed as a part of a procedure on the tummy area.

How it's done

The anaesthetic may be local, regional (via an epidural injection) or general, depending on the area treated, the technique being used and the recommendation made by your surgeon. Once the anaesthetic has been given, small 5mm incisions are made around the area to be treated. A hollow suction tube (cannula) is then inserted and moved around under the skin to break up unwanted fat. The fat is removed either manually with a large

syringe, or else with the use of a vacuum pump. A thin blanket of fat is left underneath the skin to help prevent rippling or bumpy skin occurring after the liposuction is over.

Time to heal

If liposuction is done under a local anaesthetic, then some pressure, movement, and stinging can be felt while the fat is being removed, but this is rarely painful. Bruising, swelling, and some blood-coloured fluid leaking from the wounds may be expected for a few days. Depending on the extent of the procedure, you may be able to return to work within a few days to a week.

Is there scarring?

There may be a little skin discolouration or scarring at the incision points, but these will fade over time.

How long will the effects last?

Although the fat cells that have been removed are gone forever, patients will still have fat cells that can expand if they gain weight after surgery. Liposuction cannot prevent weight gain nor is it a treatment for cellulite. Around 30% of patients require a repeat procedure in order to achieve or maintain the desired result.

Is it safe?

Possible complications include infection, numbness, nerve damage and persistent swelling.

The liposuction has removed excess areas of flab and fat

£ LIPOSUCTION PRICE

£1,000-£5,000 depending upon the number and size of areas being treated

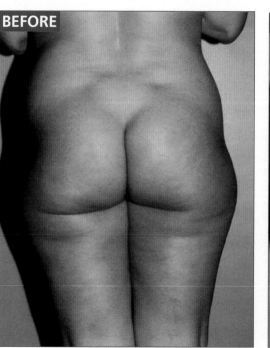

BEFORE

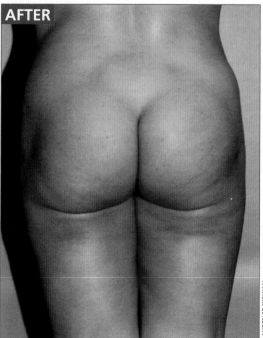

AFTER

LAURENCE KIRWAN

Lumpiness at the site of the liposuction can occur, but only very rarely. In extremely rare circumstancess, more serious complications can include blood clots and severe infections.

What should I ask?

How much weight can be removed with this procedure? Should I aim to lower my body weight before treatment? Would I also need a tummy tuck to achieve the desired results? How many sites will need liposuction?

Is it right for me?

This treatment is ideal for patients with stubborn fat around the stomach, back, chest, hips, buttocks, thighs, knees, upper arms, underneath the chin and the neck. The best candidates are average weight people with firm, elastic skin who have pockets of fat in specific areas. Older people with less elastic skin should not expect the same results as younger people with firmer bodies.

Contraindications

A tummy tuck may be more appropriate for patients with an excess of sagging skin.

ALTERNATIVE LIPOSUCTION PROCEDURES

Fluid Injection

● One alternative to the traditional liposuction technique is fluid injection, which involves injecting a solution of lignocaine (an anaesthetic) and adrenaline (a drug that contracts blood vessels to reduce bleeding) into the fatty areas before liposuction.

● This allows the fat to be removed more easily, reduces blood loss, bruising, and provides local anaesthesia before and after treatment, reducing pain and discomfort.

Tumescent Liposuction

● This involves large volumes of fluid – around three times the amount of fat to be removed – being injected into the fatty area.

● This is usually performed on patients who only need a local anaesthetic, but it usually takes much longer to do the treatment, sometimes up to 4-5 hours for large areas of fat removal.

Super-Wet

● The super-wet technique is similar to the tumescent technique, except that less fluid is used. This is usually done under a sedative injected into the vein, or via a general anaesthetic, and typically takes 1-2 hours.

LOWER BODY LIFT
(BELT LIPECTOMY)

GOOD FOR?
- ☑ stomach
- ☑ hips
- ☑ buttocks
- ☑ thighs
- ☑ lower back

What is it?

A lower body lift can dramatically improve the appearance of droopy buttocks and sagging thighs and stomachs. It removes excess skin and fat from the abdomen, hips and lower back, to lift the buttocks and outer thighs and tighten the underlying muscles of the abdominal wall. It's designed primarily for patients who have lost large amounts of weight and are left with saggy and unattractive skin around the stomach, buttocks, thighs and hips.

How it's done

Lower body lifts are usually performed under a general anaesthetic. Crescent-shaped segments of skin and fat are removed from the buttock and thigh areas. The remaining skin and tissue is then lifted to achieve a tighter and smoother effect. This procedure is also often combined with a tummy tuck or liposuction to achieve the desired effect. A lower body lift will usually take around 4–5 hours, depending on whether any other procedures such as liposuction are involved.

Time to heal

There is quite a high level of pain and discomfort during the healing process, and bruising after the surgery is very visible. Swelling is severe and can take up to 3–4 months to disappear. You may also experience numbness of the skin around the buttocks and thighs and it may take several months for the sensation to return. You will need to stay in hospital for 1 or 2 days, then it generally takes two weeks or longer to recover from a lower body lift. It will be about six weeks before you can go back to vigorous exercise.

'A lower body lift can dramatically improve the appearance of droopy buttocks and sagging thighs. It removes excess skin and fat to tighten the underlying muscles of the abdominal wall. It's designed primarily for patients who have lost large amounts of weight and are left with saggy and unattractive skin'

>>

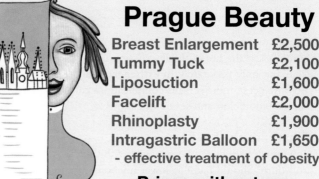

>> LOWER BODY LIFT

Is there scarring?
Long scars may stretch across the upper buttocks, outer and inner thighs. Wherever possible, these are positioned so that underwear can hide them. Scars may appear to worsen initially but will flatten out and lighten in colour over time.

How long will the effects last?
Results are permanent, although future weight gain will cause skin to stretch and undo the surgeon's good work. Liposuction or a tummy tuck can be performed alongside a lower body lift to improve the overall result.

Is it safe?
Very rarely, complications can include infection, a reaction to the anaesthetic, blood or fluid collection underneath the skin, nerve damage or blood clots. In rare circumstances, the lymph gland system in the groin is interrupted during surgery, resulting in severe swelling which will subside after a few weeks.

What should I ask?
Would liposuction or a tummy tuck give the result I am looking for? Should I have a combination of treatments? Is this the right procedure for me?

Is it right for me?
The best candidates are individuals with obvious saggy skin in the stomach, back, thigh, hip and buttock areas. This looseness may be the result of normal ageing, of many pregnancies, or of significant weight loss.

Contraindications
If you have had phlebitis (inflamed blood vessels) in either of your legs, you may not be a candidate for lift surgery.

> **£ LOWER BODY LIFT PRICE**
> From £4,000 per procedure, plus £1,000+ for additional liposuction if required

MINI-TUMMY TUCK

What is it?
A mini-tummy tuck removes fat deposits from the area below the navel to leave a flatter, smoother body profile and younger-looking abdomen. This is similar to a full tummy tuck (abdominoplasty) but is a less complex procedure as the navel does not need repositioning.

How it's done
Mini tummy tucks are usually performed under a general anaesthetic. Alternatives include an epidural anaesthetic injection which will numb the area from the waist down, combined with a sedative to make you drowsy, so that you remain awake but feel very little discomfort. A large cut is made which runs across the lower abdomen, just above the pubic area. The skin is then lifted from the abdominal wall up to the navel. Fat deposits are removed and the skin is stretched down to the incision line, with the excess skin removed before it is restitched. The navel is not repositioned. The procedure takes 1–2 hours, depending on whether any liposuction is involved.

GOOD FOR?
☑ flabby lower stomach with sagging skin

Time to heal
Some people return to work after two weeks, while others will prefer to take three or four weeks to rest and recouperate.

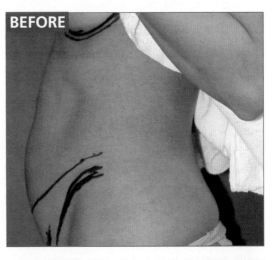
BEFORE

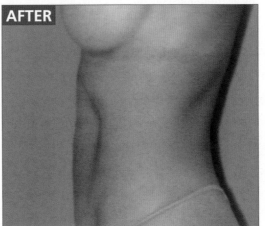
AFTER

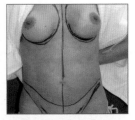
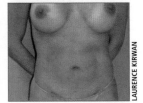

The mini-tummy tuck has smoothed down the stomach and made it flatter

LAURENCE KIRWAN

>>

COSMETIC SURGERY

>> MINI-TUMMY TUCK

For the first few days following surgery the abdomen will feel swollen and tight with some pain and discomfort. At first you may not be able to stand up straight without feeling a tugging sensation, but you should start walking as soon as possible. Bruising after the surgery is usually quite light but swelling is substantial and it can take up to three months to disappear. You may also experience numbness of the abdominal skin and it may take several months for the sensation to return.

Is there scarring?
The surgery does produce a permanent scar which extends from hip to hip. Scars will worsen at first but heal within 9-12 months. While they'll never disappear completely, abdominal scars will not show under most clothing.

How long will the effects last?
The effects of a mini-tummy tuck are generally long-lasting provided you follow a balanced diet and exercise regularly. If you put on weight after the surgery this will affect the results.

Is it safe?
Possible complications include infection, a reaction to the anaesthesia, blood or fluid collection underneath the skin, nerve damage or blood clots. However, these are all very rare and happen in only a small percentage of patients.

What should I ask?
Could I get the results I want from liposuction? Do I need a full abdominoplasty to achieve my desired result? Would liposuction be needed to remove fat deposits from my hips? Should I combine this with another procedure?

Is it right for me?
The procedure is ideal for patients who are less than 15% over their ideal body weight but who are carrying excess weight on their stomach below the navel.

Contraindications
Women planning a future pregnancy may be poor candidates for a mini-tummy tuck as tightened skin and muscle will stretch during pregnancy.

£

MINI-TUMMY TUCK PRICE
From £3,000-£6,000 depending on the surgeon (the upper price limit usually includes liposuction)

TUMMY TUCK (ABDOMINOPLASTY)

What is it?
A tummy tuck removes excess skin and fat from the middle and lower area of the abdomen in order to tighten the muscles of the abdominal wall and reduce the appearance of a saggy or sticking-out stomach.

How it's done
Tummy tucks are usually performed under a general anaesthetic. During the operation, a large cut is made which runs across the lower abdomen, usually from hip-bone to hip-bone, just above the pubic area. A second incision is then made to free

the navel (belly button) from surrounding tissue. The skin is then separated from the abdominal wall all the way up to the ribcage to reveal the abdominal muscles. The muscles are pulled and tightened and stitched into position to provide a firmer abdominal wall, which provides the foundation for a slimmer waistline. Fat deposits may also be removed. The skin is then stretched down, excess skin is removed and the skin is stitched up. A new hole is usually cut for the navel, which is stitched back into place. The procedure takes between 2 and 5 hours. The larger the amount of fat, the longer it will take.

GOOD FOR?
☑ sagging stomach
☑ stomach that sticks out
☑ stretch marks

The tummy tuck removes excess flab and tightens the stomach muscles

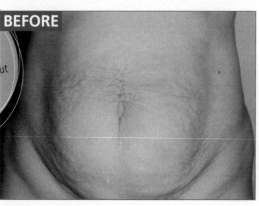

BEFORE

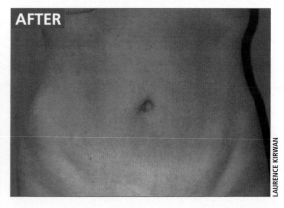

AFTER

LAURENCE KIRWAN

Time to heal

Patients are usually home within a couple of days but it may take up to six weeks before you can resume normal activities. Following surgery, the abdomen will feel swollen and tight with some pain and discomfort and standing up straight will be difficult. Expect light bruising and substantial swelling which may take up to three months to disappear. The abdomen often feels numb for several weeks post-surgery. You will need to return for surface stitches or staples to be removed after 5-7 days, when you will be given an abdominal support garment to wear for several weeks.

Is there scarring?

The surgery produces a permanent scar that extends from hip to hip. Scars may appear to worsen during the first 3-6 months as they heal, but will flatten out and lighten in colour within a year. The scars won't show under most clothing.

How long will the effects last?

The results are long-lasting providing that patients do not put on weight, which will stretch the skin.

Is it safe?

Possible but rare complications can include infection, a reaction to the anaesthesia, blood or fluid collection underneath the skin, nerve damage, blood clots, and an irregular or a lopsided appearance after the operation.

What should I ask?

Would liposuction create the effects I want? Would a mini-tummy tuck work? What if I become pregnant after the procedure?

Is it right for me?

The best candidates are those within 15% of their ideal body weight who have loose skin or weak muscles around their abdomen and wish to restore a youthful body shape. It is right for women whose skin and muscle have been stretched by pregnancy, or who have had significant weight loss, leaving loose and overhanging skin.

Contraindications

This operation is not recommended for women who intend to become pregnant in the future.

> **TUMMY TUCK PRICE**
> From £3,000-£6,000 depending on the surgeon and the amount of excess skin to be removed. The upper price limit usually includes liposuction

>> TUMMY TUCK CASE STUDY

Patient: Sharon Betts, 46, housewife
Type of treatment: tummy tuck with liposuction

Q Why did you choose to have this procedure?

A After my first child, I had a really overhanging stomach where the skin had stretched an awful lot. After my second child it looked even worse. I went to see the doctor who explained my condition was known as an 'apron stomach' and is actually quite common after having children. The muscles stretch so much that no amount of diet and exercise will get them back to normal shape. The doctor explained I would need a tummy tuck and liposuction on my hips and stomach to amend the problem but the NHS waiting list was two years long. I lost enough weight to get me to my ideal size and decided I couldn't wait any longer.

Q Where did you go for surgery?

A I called round some UK surgeons for quotes and found out the procedure I needed would cost between £7,500-£10,500 over here – far too much for my savings. Then I heard about the Elyzea clinic from a friend. They have a clinic in Belgium where costs are much lower so they can perform procedures at reduced prices. I went for a consultation at their Harley Street clinic and booked in straight away.

Q How did you feel during and after surgery?

A When I came round from the general anaesthetic, I felt shaky and in a lot of pain but the medication helped. Considering the extent of the surgery I was actually expecting to be in a lot more pain. I was out of bed within three days and only needed two weeks off work. At first I was hunched when walking around as you need to give the stomach muscles time to stretch but I was active fairly quickly.

Q What impact has the treatment had on your life?

A I am now another half a stone lighter, I have a much tighter and more toned stomach and all my stretch marks are gone – my stomach is flatter than before I had the kids! I have slight scars but they are positioned under my bikini line so no-one can see them. I am so pleased with the results and would recommend the procedure. It has really boosted my confidence and given me the motivation to exercise to keep looking trim.

Q What advice do you have for someone considering this surgery?

A I would advise anyone considering the procedure to go to someone qualified and have a thorough consultation first, so you can find the right combination of procedures that will give you the results you want.

BEFORE

Sharon is now half a stone lighter

AFTER

ELYZEA CLINIC

Have the ageless smile you always wanted... created with a fusion of beauty and function...

 **Care Dental** makes it happen for you..

Your smile influences virtually every aspect of your life, from the impressions you make on others in business and social environments, to your sense of confidence and self-esteem. At Caredental Smile Studios your smile will definitely shine with confidence.

2 Years 0% interest available!*
Terms and conditions apply

Success rate of 98% speaks for itself

Call us today on 020 8570 2526 and book your FREE consultation

Member
AMERICAN ACADEMY OF COSMETIC DENTISTRY®

INVESTORS IN PEOPLE UK

Care Dental - 305 Bath Road - Hounslow - TW3 3DB
www.caredental.co.uk

6

the teeth

COSMETIC DENTISTRY

A clean white smile instantly brightens a face, but teeth naturally discolour with age, and the accumulative effects of smoking, drinking tea, coffee and red wine, as well as eating rich spicy foods, cause staining and yellowing. Gums can also shrink, exposing more of the tooth than we'd like. Fortunately, cosmetic dentistry in the UK is following in the footsteps of the US, which means a whole range of procedures are now available to correct even the most extreme cosmetic dental problems.

Teeth whitening

introduction to

A recent large-scale study by the British Dental Health Foundation revealed that one in two adults approaching middle age would consider having cosmetic dentistry to improve their appearance

cosmetic dentistry

DISCOVER THE PERFECT SMILE

A WHITE YOUTHFUL SMILE is crucial for women who want to look and feel younger, and a recent large-scale study by the British Dental Health Foundation revealed that one in two adults approaching middle age would consider having cosmetic dentistry to improve their appearance. The smile is fundamental to the face, and having a perfect one can make all the difference.

Around 84 per cent of dentists now offer cosmetic procedures. The range of treatments include whitening, gum grafting/contouring and dental face lifts. In-salon whitening treatments produce faster and longer-lasting results than at-home whitening systems, although these are more affordable. Gum grafting and contouring can help restore receding gums or trim away excess gum tissue, while the dental face lift uses veneers and sometimes implants and bridges to correct gaps, staining or overcrowded teeth.

Choosing the right cosmetic dentist can be just as important as choosing the right treatment, and cosmetic dentist Mark Hughes has this advice: 'Check your dentist is a member of the American and British Academies of Cosmetic Dentistry, and ensure he or she has 10 years of training in a practice that focuses on cosmetic dentistry every day. At your consultation you should ask for testimonials, before and after photos and, lastly, you should follow your gut instinct, as it is important to trust your dentist.'

Read on for more detailed information about the various cosmetic dentistry procedures available that could provide you with the perfect smile.

WHAT THE DENTISTS SAY

- Cosmetic dentist Joe Oliver says that women can easily knock 10 years off their age with cosmetic dentistry: *'A fresh clean lasting smile always lifts a face and with dentistry people can find their teeth look better than they did in their twenties.'*

- While cosmetic dentistry used to be associated with wealth and fame, Dr Anthony Zybutz says that it is now accessible to everybody: *'Cosmetic dentistry is for anyone desiring to look younger, improve the quality of their smile and their self-esteem.'*

- Dr Michael Carling adds that when women see how good their teeth can look it encourages them to improve their overall appearance: *'Women feel more elegant after cosmetic surgery and, when the compliments follow, they start to think about how they can change their clothes, the rest of their face and even their haircut.'*

- Zybutz says that women are also more likely to look after their teeth following cosmetic dentistry: *'Once they have seen the benefits of a healthy smile, oral health becomes a priority.'*

YOUR GUIDE TO THE RANGE AND TYPE OF PROCEDURES >>

DENTISTRY

gums

Gums can recede as we age, making teeth appear longer and less attractive. Could a gum procedure help you to look younger?

GRAFTING & CONTOURING

What's involved?

Grafting is a procedure where tissue is grafted from one part of the mouth, generally the roof, and stitched to the receding gum. One tooth or one section of the mouth is treated. Grafting is usually carried out under general anaesthetic and takes one to one and a half hours. Gums have to be in good health before treatment and you will be advised to use rinses ahead of the operation. Grafting is often combined with a contouring procedure that involves trimming and reshaping the gums, commonly using a soft tissue laser because of its predictable results and the fact that it allows fast healing. The contouring generally adds 20-40 minutes on to the procedure time.

Time to heal

The mouth will be quite sore and tender after the grafting and it will take around three months for full healing. Your dentist will give you a special wash to use after the procedure to keep your mouth clean and will also advise you on your diet. You will be asked to use a soft toothbrush while the tissues naturally attach and tighten. The contouring aspect of the procedure heals much more quickly – usually a couple of days – as the laser seals the blood vessels in the gums so that the tissue can heal with relatively little discomfort.

GOOD FOR?

☑ gums that have receded, making more of the teeth visible, so they seem longer and less attractive

How long will the effects last?

Grafting is an uncommon procedure and there aren't any long-term studies into results. However, you can expect the gums to shrink with time so that you need further treatment in under 10 years. The results of gum contouring are usually permanent. Sometimes a dentist may remove too much gum tissue, however, leading to swelling and the need for further corrective treatment.

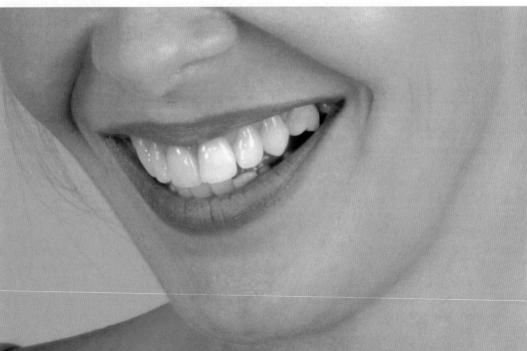

A perfect smile can make all the difference to your face

£ **GRAFTING COSTS BETWEEN**
£600-£1,200

CONTOURING COSTS FROM
£120

DAVID WIGMORE

DENTISTRY

smile

Smile lifts – also known as dental face lifts – are designed to correct gaps and stained or overcrowded teeth, using a combination of techniques to surgically enhance your smile

SMILE LIFT (DENTAL FACE LIFT)

What's involved?

Porcelain or laminate veneers are placed over existing teeth to change tooth colour, shape and arrangement. During the consultation, a dentist may take a photo of your teeth and manipulate it on screen using Computer Imaging Technology to show you what the achievable results are. An impression is made of the teeth and temporary plastic veneers are made. Teeth are contoured and the surface layer of enamel is removed so that the temporary veneers can be fitted using special light-cured glues. Around two weeks later you will need to return to the surgery when permanent veneers will be fitted. The dental face lift can sometimes be combined with the fitting of bridges and implants to correct gaps in the teeth. The entire process can take as little as two weeks.

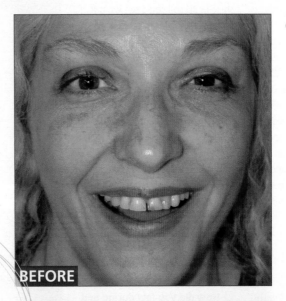

BEFORE

JOE OLIVER

GOOD FOR?

- ☑ gappy teeth
- ☑ stained teeth
- ☑ overcrowded teeth
- ☑ receding gums
- ☑ misshapen teeth

'Veneers, if done correctly, are the strongest, most beautiful and lasting type of restoration'

Dr Anthony Zybutz

Time to heal

You should expect to experience some gum tenderness and mild sensitivity to hot and cold food and drinks for a few days. Also, your teeth and 'bite' may feel strange to start with as you get used to the veneers, but this will pass over time.

How long will the effects last?

Porcelain veneers can last for 10–15 years while plastic veneers usually last around 5–7 years.

AFTER

The difference made by the smile lift is astounding

£ **PRICE**
From £125-£1,000 per tooth, depending on the material used. Expect to pay up to £15,000

'The smile stretches all the way back so you may need most of your teeth done'

Mark Hughes, cosmetic dentist

VENEERS

- There are two types of veneer available – plastic and porcelain.
- Plastic veneers can be made in the dental surgery in a single visit.
- Plastic veneers can be colour matched directly to your teeth and shaped to suit the shape of your own teeth.
- Porcelain is less easy to shape, but it lasts longer and is more resistant to staining.
- Sometimes veneers are made very thin so that the colour of the natural teeth can be picked up. If teeth are heavily stained, the veneers can be made thicker to mask this.

\>\>

>> SMILE CASE STUDY

Patient: Bridget O'Brien, housewife
Treatment type: smile dental face lift

Q Why did you choose this particular treatment?

A I was very unhappy with the shape of my teeth, as well as with all the stains on them and their overall worn appearance. My teeth were really crowded together and my whole mouth just looked too narrow, especially on the right hand side. One of my friends had undergone dental surgery and recommended the Thurloe Street surgery very enthusiastically.

Q Where did you get treatment and who administered it?

A I went to the Thurloe Street Dental Group and was treated by cosmetic dentist Dr Raza, with whom I had a very thorough and encouraging initial consultation. He took a photo of my smile and manipulated it on a computer in front of me. We planned to whiten and resize my teeth, as well as correct the crowding, widen the arch and add some natural effects, like a warmer colour near the necks of my teeth. He even showed me the proposed

smile in 3D so I could see what it would look like from every angle.

Q How long did it take?

A Well, after the consultation he then gave me a temporary treatment, so that I could show my friends and family and see what they said about it. He treated 10 upper teeth with a combination of four porcelain crowns and six porcelain veneers. I only wore these for a few days before going back to fine tune the design. I didn't actually make any changes though, because I was very happy with how my smile was starting to look.

Q How did you feel during and after treatment? How did you look immediately afterwards?

A Wearing the temporaries was fine – there weren't any problems at all. Fitting the permanent porcelain veneers and crowns was fine too, and the procedure wasn't the least bit painful. I loved the new look straight away, and my family all agreed wholeheartedly! I felt much happier immediately, as the thing I'd been so unhappy about for years was finally fixed!

BEFORE

Bridget felt much more confident after her smile lift procedure

AFTER

HAIDER RAZA

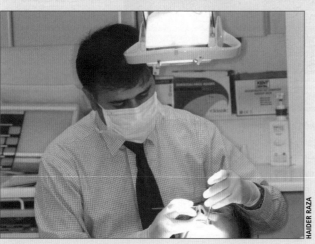

HAIDER RAZA

Q Did you suffer any negative side effects?

A No. I suppose it took a little while to get used to the veneers, and eating felt a bit weird at first, but that passed very quickly. Certainly, there was nothing painful involved.

Q What impact has the treatment had on your life?

A I am absolutely delighted with my new look and it's so nice to be able to beam a massive smile at everyone I meet! It's definitely been worth it, and the effect it's had on my own confidence has been astounding.

Q Do you have any advice for anyone considering this treatment?

A Make sure you have a thorough consultation with an experienced cosmetic dentist who can take you through it all and show you exactly what the results should look like.

'Patients freqently tell us their lives have changed because of their new smiles'

Dr Haider Raza

teeth whitening

With Britain increasingly going the way of the US, more and more people are in search of that perfect, brilliant, movie star white smile...

AT-HOME WHITENING

What's involved

At-home systems have the benefit of allowing you to whiten your teeth in the convenience of your own home, although the British Dental Health Foundation recommends visiting a dentist first to check your teeth are suitable for the treatment. Tooth whitening will only lighten natural teeth and not dental fillings, veneers or crowns. The kits come with a custom mouthpiece, which you can warm in water for a couple of minutes and then place over teeth and allow it to cool and shrink to fit around the teeth. The mouthpiece is lined with a gel that usually contains carbomide peroxide.

Tooth whitening can make a huge difference to stained teeth

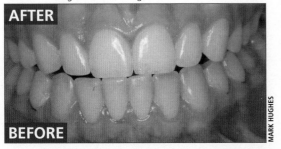

AFTER

BEFORE

MARK HUGHES

How long does it take?

It takes around five minutes to mould the mouthpiece and then it is worn between two and six hours a day. Effects are noticeable after a couple of treatments but it can take up to 10 days to achieve full results. Teethwhite is a tooth whitening company that provides home-kits in three different strengths: regular, rapid and ultra rapid. Each kit produces the same results but over different periods of time. Regular strength is the least concentrated and is recommended for people with sensitive teeth.

Time to heal

Some people experience some tooth sensitivity during and after treatment, although this usually settles a couple of days later and can be soothed by using toothpaste for sensitive teeth.

How long will the effects last?

Effects can last up to two years although this is dependent on diet and lifestyle. Smoking and drinking a lot of tea, coffee and red wine or eating lots of curry, for example, can shorten the time.

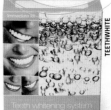

TEETHWHITE

GOOD FOR?

☑ teeth that have been stained or discoloured, largely by smoking, drinking wine, tea and coffee

£ PRICE

Up to around £300. Teethwhite charges £99 for its Regular whitening kit, £129 for Rapid and £169 for the Ultra Rapid kit

PROFESSIONAL TEETH WHITENING

What's involved

You should start by having an initial consultation, when you can ask questions and your dentist can explain what to expect from the whitening procedure. Then, impressions will be made of the teeth and sent to a laboratory to be formed into plastic trays. Before whitening begins, a thick liquid is applied to teeth and gums to prevent the bleach from damaging the tissue. The gel, usually hydrogen peroxide, is applied to the trays which are then placed against the teeth. Many dentists also use a laser or UV light to heat the gel and speed up the lightening process.

How long does it take?

The whitening procedure lasts around an hour. Most dentists also recommend and provide at-home whitening systems to maximise results over the next week or so.

Time to heal

Wearing the plastic trays isn't painful but you're aware they're there. Teeth can be sensitive during or after treatment for a couple of days. Toothpaste for sensitive teeth can ease symptoms.

How long does it last?

Up to two years. The length of time whitening lasts is also down to lifestyle. Smoking and drinking a lot of tea, coffee and red wine can all reduce the lasting time.

BEFORE

AFTER

ANTHONY ZYBUTZ

DID YOU KNOW?

There was a health scare in 1999 about the use of hydrogen peroxide in cosmetic tooth whitening. The consensus is now clear, however, that it poses no risks when it is supervised by a qualified dentist and is medically prescribed.

£ PRICE

Around £40 for a single tooth, up to £500 for the whole mouth

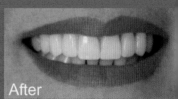

>> HOME WHITENING CASE STUDY

Patient: Charlotte Reddington, part-time model and student
Treatment type: home whitening

Charlotte wore the gum shield for four hours, every other day

Q Why did you choose this treatment?

A I've always been concerned about my teeth. They're naturally straight but were quite yellow and stained as a result of smoking and eating lots of curries. I also model part-time and was aware that most of the celebrities in magazines have bright white teeth, so when I heard about Teethwhite I decided to give it a go. I was looking for an easy quick-fix solution, and the idea of home whitening really appealed because of its convenience. I have also always been a little bit scared of the dentist, so this was a great way to get around making an appointment! I heard about

Teethwhite through a friend and sent off for the kit, which arrived with a gum shield, mould, gel and instructions.

Q How long did it take?

A After heating the gum shield and biting into the soft mould for my top and bottom set of teeth, I lined the shield with the gel. I then put the mould into my mouth and bit down on it. I wore it for four hours the first time and then wore it every other day, rinsing it and replacing the gel each time. Friends noticed a change to the colour of my teeth after three applications but I continued wearing the shield, usually over-night, for around two weeks until

I was happy with the change in tooth colour.

Q How did you feel during treatment and how did you look afterwards? Were there any negative side effects?

A I experienced very slight sensitivity in my teeth immediately after the first application but it wasn't actually painful. It also took me a while to get used to having the shield in my mouth, but I gradually stopped being aware that it was even there. I am over the moon with the results. The kit is in a neat compact case too so it takes up little space.

The kit comprises a gum shield, mould, gel and instructions

Q What impact has treatment had on your life?

A Whitening my teeth has really boosted my confidence and I'm no longer afraid to smile. I'm so glad I did it and would recommend it to anyone. It is great for my work as a model too.

Q Do you have any advice for others considering this treatment?

A My advice to others is to just do it. I am always telling my friends to whiten their teeth too and there really is no need to worry about sensitivity. It doesn't hurt and it is definitely worth it.

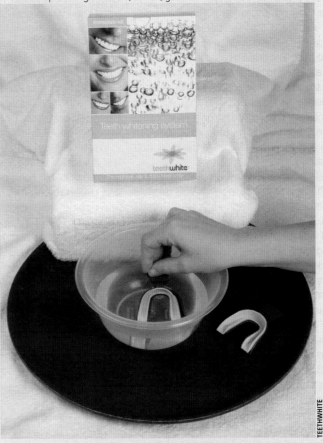

Does this man hold the secret to younger looking skin?

You may take one look at James Greenwell, Managing Director of the on-Group, and think 'how can anyone so young know anything about anti-ageing' well, what this man does not know about anti-ageing is not worth knowing.

A former international athlete and ex captain of the GB Modern Pentathlon squad, James found he was getting inflamed tendons from all the training and nothing seemed to make any difference to the injury, no matter what he tried. He was fast losing hope and, at 29, wasn't getting any younger. Eventually, he started to think the injury would force him out of the sport he loved, until he discovered collagen as a natural nutritional supplement.

"Within 22 days of taking 100% pure collagen, I was able to train again on a daily basis - and the injury hasn't recurred. It was truly amazing" he says.

James was so impressed with the speed of his recovery that he decided to make this natural supplement available to others. At first his idea was to supply it to other athletes to aid recovery from sports injuries and as he researched the product in order to sell it, he found that not only does collagen help repair and regenerate muscles, bones and tendons but collagen is also a vital protein found in the skin, hair and nails.

"We all produce collagen naturally, but from the age of 25, collagen levels deplete at a rate of 1.5% per year" says James "This contributes to skin losing its elasticity and hair and nails becoming brittle. By the age of 45 our collagen level has decreased by 30% Numerous clinical studies have shown that collagen helps prevent degenerative conditions such as osteoarthritis and osteoporosis" he continues " There are absolutely no harmful side effects and the products have been tested and approved by doctors and dermotologists all over the world."

James started to build a business around the supply of natural health products. His company, on-Nutrition, quickly became one of the leading suppliers of collagen capsules and the success stories of those taking it started flooding in.

" The more James looked into the research and findings on collagen the more impressed he became with its anti-ageing properties, so much that he created a sister company, On-Beauty, and formulated an anti-ageing skin care range called proto-Col with collagen and coral.

I was inspired by the benefits of collagen to create a range of skincare products that really would make a difference to your skin at a price that you can afford."

2 years on and proto-Col is one of the fastest growing luxury brands in the world that is used by celebrities such as Jennifer Aniston, Dame Judi Dench, Cat Deeley and Nicky Haslam. The proto-Col range is available from selected salons around the country (including Green Street House here in Bath) and most recently proto-Col were signed by Harrods for the infamous 5th floor Urban Retreat. The range is also distributed in Europe, Bangkok, USA and Russia with plans this year to expand to New Zealand and Australia. James also works with the Ideal World Shopping Channel and has become the fastest selling product on the channel this year.

" We have worked constantly over the last 2 years to build the proto-Col brand and now to be recognised by Harrods and Urban Retreat as one of the leading anti-ageing skin care products is just wonderful. In just two years we have achieved a turnover in excess of two million pounds" You would think that James would be happy to sit back now and enjoy the success but no, " I want proto-Col to be a household name, for it to be an internationally recognised brand and to give the answer they have been looking for in the quest for younger looking skin". So, does this man hold the secret to younger looking skin?... We certainly think so.

For more information phone head office on 0870 770 3861 or log on www.on-beauty.co.uk

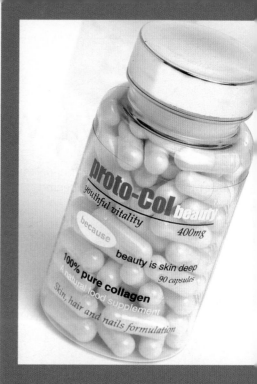

7

lifestyle

DIET, EXERCISE, HAIR, WELL-BEING

What you eat and drink, the way you live and how you exercise and cope with stress all have lasting effects on the way you feel and look. A holistic approach to well-being can wipe years from your appearance, and in this section you will find a guide to the methods that work: superfoods and supplements to recharge your energy and improve your skin tone and hair, body-sculpting exercises and rejuvenating natural facials, and relaxation techniques to boost beauty sleep and positivity.

introduction to

you

Diet, exercise and relaxation help turn back the clock in ways that no other anti-ageing treatment can, making you feel young from the inside out

lifestyle

FIND NEW WAYS TO FEEL YOUNGER

DIET, EXERCISE AND relaxation help turn back the clock in ways that no other anti-ageing treatment can, making you feel young from the inside out.

Some foods are more effective than others in the fight against ageing, due to their anti-oxidant properties which help to protect the body. Fruit and vegetables in particular contain a potent anti-oxidant mix of vitamins, minerals and phytochemicals (plant nutrients) that have more health-giving results when ingested together in food than when added to a pot of skin cream.

The rush of energy that follows an exercise session is always rejuvenating: you step out with extra bounce and a surge of endorphins (feel-good brain chemicals) that inspire self-confidence. When you feel this good inside you look good: you stand taller, your shoulders drop away from your ears as tense muscles release, your chest opens, helping you breathe in more energising oxygen and exhale toxins more effectively. You might even smile – the most rejuvenating tonic there is! People who exercise report fewer sleep problems and seem to cope better with stressful events than those who don't. And lack of sleep and stress show visibly on the face and in a tense, stooped posture, adding years to your appearance. This section features body-shaping exercises designed to target specific problem areas of the body and face, from the upper arms and chin to thighs, bum and tummy.

Ageing takes its toll on our hair too, with greying, thinning and hair loss all telling a tale we'd rather that nobody knew. Our guide will show you, however, how to rediscover your natural colour and grow a fuller head of hair, as well as delve into different hair styles to find the one that suits you best.

Finally we look at lifestyle strategies to restore inner and outer youthfulness. Stress befuddles the memory and cognitive functioning, and there's nothing like feeling muddled and forgetful to make you feel older than your years. There are ways to destress the body, calm the mind and promote positivity, including easy meditation and breathing exercises, as well as strategies that will ensure you get a full night's sleep. There is also a selection of complementary alternative therapies to treat yourself with that should leave you feeling refreshed and renewed in body, mind and spirit.

KICK THE HABIT

If there's one thing you can do to make yourself look and feel younger, it's to stop smoking. Smoking makes the diseases we associate with age – heart disease, stroke, lung problems and cancers – that much more likely to affect you. For more information and help on quitting, turn to page 167.

GOODSHOOT

TIP

Aim for colour on your plate – mix dark green, orange, yellow and red vegetables as much as possible

A-Z OF SUPERFOODS

The elixir of life that can turn back the clock and keep us youthful has been sought since time began, yet scientists now realise the answer may lie in the foods we eat. Many so-called 'superfoods' contain substances that are vital for health, and which can ward off diseases that lead to premature ageing. Many fruit, vegetables, nuts and seeds contain essential oils or weak plant hormones (isoflavones) that can help keep your skin looking youthful, while eating a diet that is as organic as possible helps to minimise the toxins your liver has to deal with on a day to day basis. Even something as simple as drinking adequate amounts of water – a minimum of 2 litres per day (8 glasses) – plays an important role by flushing through detox organs, improving skin hydration and helping to keep your joints lubricated.

Scientists recently announced in the British Medical Journal that regularly eating just seven superfoods – fish, fruit, vegetables, garlic, almonds, dark chocolate and wine – can reduce your risk of a heart attack or stroke by a massive 76%. Furthermore, these scientists predict that eating these foods on a daily basis (fish 2 to 4 times per week) can increase life expectancy by six and a half years for men, and five years for women.

The foods with the strongest anti-ageing effect are those containing anti-oxidants – substances that help to neutralise the chemical reactions responsible for many ageing processes in the body. As well as anti-oxidants, fibre, vitamins and minerals, fruit and vegetables contain protective plant substances known as phytochemicals which help to protect against cancer.

Take a look at the foods you should aim to consume on a regular basis. Some, such as tea and citrus fruits, are familiar. Others, such as papaya and sweet potatoes, are a little more exotic but delicious and easy to get used to.

'Eating a diet that is as organic as possible helps to minimise the toxins your liver has to deal with on a day to day basis'

LIVING FOODS AND SPROUTED SEEDS

- Eating your food raw seems to be the best way to absorb dietary nutrients for an optimum, anti-ageing effect.

- As well as avoiding the heat-destruction of vitamins, enzymes and other beneficial substances, the body is better able to digest and absorb nutrients in their raw state.

- Home sprouted seeds (ie seeds you've allowed to germinate at home) are a great source of vitamins, minerals, trace elements and live enzymes, adding delicious nutrients and crunch to your diet.

- Sprouted beans are easily produced at home in jam jars or customised germinators (eg BioSnacky germinator from healthfood stores or www.bioforce. co.uk) which provide the right warmth and humidity for optimal growth.

- Rinse 4-6 tablespoons mixed organic seeds in water. Sprinkle lightly over a germinator or add to a glass jar, and allow to germinate for 3–5 days.

- Good seeds include: red-clover, alfalfa, radish, mung bean, broccoli, cress, wheat, lentil, quinoa, mustard.

- Add sprouted seeds to any food, like salads, rice, soups, chicken and fish.

ALMONDS

Almonds contain a combination of proteins, fibre and monounsaturated fats (similar to those found in olive oil) that, together, help to lower total cholesterol levels and reduce your risk of coronary heart disease and stroke by over 12%. Scientists recently suggested eating a handful (68g) per day for optimum health. The essential oils present in almonds will help to moisturise your skin and hair from the inside, too.

APRICOTS

Apricots are a rich source of orange-yellow plant pigments known as carotenoids. Obtaining around 6mg mixed carotenoids per day can help to reduce your risk of cancer, but most people only get around 2mg carotenoids per day from their diet. Eat a handful of dried apricots as a healthy snack two or three times a week. Carotenoids also have a beneficial anti-oxidant effect on skin, where they become concentrated (in fact eating too many can lead to temporary orange discolouration of skin).

AVOCADO

As well as being a good source of vitamins C, E and betacarotene, avocados contain a factor that stimulates growth of youthful skin. Some varieties of avocado provide as much as 80% of their energy content in the form of vegetable oils, of which most is in the form of monounsaturated fatty acids which have beneficial effects on blood fat levels and the circulation. Avocados also contain a type of sugar that helps to satisfy sensations of hunger. Aim to eat one avocado per week.

'Scientists recently suggested eating a handful of almonds per day for optimum health'

GLOSSARY

● **free radicals** are unstable molecules that cause reactions in your body responsible for premature ageing
● **anti-oxidants** patrol the body, getting rid of the harmful free radicals
● **beta-carotene** is an anti-oxidant that can help protect the body from free radicals
● **carotenoids** are organic matter that occurs naturally in plants and can protect against cancer and sun damage
● **flavonoids** are found in plants and are powerful anti-oxidants
● **isoflavones** are powerful anti-oxidants
● **phytochemicals** are any nutrient from a plant source that has a beneficial effect on the body, whilst not being essential for its growth

BLUEBERRIES

Blueberries contain useful amounts of anti-oxidants, although not as many as the closely related bilberry (the bilberry can be a bit harder to track down when you're out shopping, though!). Blueberry anti-oxidants can strengthen blood vessel walls, reduce unwanted blood clots and may also help to ward off thread veins. Their blue-red pigments are also highly beneficial for your eyesight, as they protect the membranes of light-sensitive cells and increase blood flow to the retina, as well as increase the strength of collagen fibres in capillaries and connective tissues. You can buy bilberry extracts over the counter (25% anthocyanosides – the powerful substance found in bilberries) and take them in quantities of 80–160mg, three times daily.

BROCCOLI

Dark green vegetables such as broccoli, spinach and spring greens are rich in vitamin C, folate and calcium. From an anti-ageing point of view, folate is important to help process homocysteine, an amino acid linked with hardening and furring up of the arteries. The calcium in broccoli is better absorbed than that found in milk, so is important to help build strong bones and protect you from osteoporosis. Broccoli also contains a phytochemical that has a powerful anti-cancer effect, especially against tumours of the digestive tract and lungs. You can prepare broccoli in many different ways: you could have itgrated, in salad, or lightly steamed (for no more than five minutes). Aim to eat it at least three times a week.

>>

TOP 5 SUPERFOODS FOR YOUR SKIN

- avocado
- cherries
- citrus fruits
- almonds
- seeds

CARROTS

Carrots contain carotenoids and a total of seven anti-cancer substances. Aim to eat a serving of carrots or drink 100ml carrot juice at least three times a week. As mentioned under apricots, carotenoids are concentrated in the skin where they provide anti-oxidant protection. They also help to maintain healthy eyes and may even improve night vision to help you see in the dark – but only if you are deficient in vitamin A, which is quite rare in the UK.

'Carrots also help to maintain healthy eyes and may even improve night vision to help you see in the dark – but only if you are deficient in vitamin A'

CHOCOLATE

Lingering over 100g of dark chocolate per day can lower your blood pressure even more than fruit and veg, and can give a 27% lower risk of circulatory problems. Chocolate gets the 'thumbs-up' as it's a rich source of polyphenols – the same anti-oxidants that give red wine and green tea their heart-friendly reputations. Research shows that dark chocolate improves glucose control, lowers blood pressure, increases your levels of 'good' HDL-cholesterol and reduces unwanted blood clotting. Scientists recently recommended eating 100g dark chocolate per day – sadly, its calorie content (510kcals) and expense makes this difficult! Go for the really dark kind containing at least 70% cocoa solids. The flavonoid anti-oxidants in dark chocolate also strengthen collagen, which is helpful for skin's elasticity.

CHERRIES

Cherries contain a phytochemical called ellagic acid that protects against cancer by blocking an enzyme needed for cancer cell growth. The flavonoid anti-oxidants they contain also strengthen collagen which promotes youthful skin. Eat them once or twice a week.

CHILLIES

Eating chillies stimulates production of natural painkillers (endorphins) in the brain and mucus in the stomach, which may protect against peptic ulcers. Chillies contain anti-oxidants, including capsaicin, that also protect against coronary heart disease, cancer and premature ageing. Phytochemicals in chilli peppers thin the blood to reduce the risk of blood clots, high blood pressure and raised cholesterol levels. They are a good source of beta-carotene and vitamin C. In some cultures, chillies are eaten every day. You should aim to eat a spicy meal at least once a week.

'Aim to eat a spicy meal at least once a week'

CITRUS FRUITS

Citrus is an excellent source of vitamin C and bioflavonoids – powerful anti-oxidants that help to protect against cancer, heart disease and inflammation. Vitamin C is also vital for healthy bones and youthful skin as it's needed to make collagen. Lemons are also a rich source of limonene – a phytochemical that protects against cancer. Using lime juice as a flavouring reduces the need for salt. Eat a piece of citrus fruit every day.

'Lemons are also a rich source of limonene – a phytochemical that protects against cancer'

CRANBERRY JUICE

Cranberries contain phytochemicals known as anti-adhesins that stop bacteria sticking to the wall of the urinary tract, so they are flushed out more easily. The same effects may reduce infection of the stomach with helicobacter pylori – a type of bacteria linked with peptic ulcers and stomach cancer. Research suggests that drinking 300ml cranberry juice per day can halve the risk of cystitis if you're prone to recurrent attacks.

FISH

Oily fish (eg salmon, mackerel, sardines, pilchards, herrings) are rich in EPA (eicosapentanoic acid), a type of fat that reduces inflammation, thins the blood, lowers cholesterol levels, reduces high blood pressure and protects against coronary heart disease. Fish oils can also halt the growth of some cancer cells. Scientists recently suggested eating a portion of fish (114g) two to four times a week to reduce the risk of heart disease by 14%. Fish oils also help to oil the joints and skin to keep them more youthful.

'Scientists recently suggested eating a portion of fish two to four times a week to reduce the risk of heart disease by 14%'

GARLIC

Garlic contains phytochemicals that protect against high cholesterol and high blood pressure, improve the circulation and reduce the risk of coronary heart disease and stroke. Eating 2.7g fresh cloves per day – each clove weighs around 1g – may not win you any friends, but can lower your total cholesterol level enough to cut your risk of a heart attack or stroke by a quarter.

GRAPES

Traditionally given during convalescence, red and black grapes contain anti-oxidants that are more powerful than vitamins C or E, including resveratrol – a phytochemical that helps to prevent hardening and furring up of the arteries. Grapes also contain ellagic acid – a phytochemical with anti-cancer properties. Eat a handful (or drink a glass of red wine) most days.

OLIVE OIL

Olive oil is a rich source of vitamin E and oleic acid, a monounsaturated fat that keeps blood cholesterol levels healthy and reduces the risk of coronary heart disease. A diet rich in olive oil has been shown to reduce the risk of coronary heart disease by 25%. When cooking, use olive oil rather than other vegetable oils, and use extra-virgin olive oil for salad dressings.

'A diet rich in olive oil has been shown to reduce the risk of coronary heart disease by 25%'

PAPAYA

Papaya is an excellent source of carotenoids, including the red pigment, lycopene, which has anti-cancer properties. It also contains an enzyme, papain, which breaks down protein and boosts digestion. Papaya is a popular anti-ageing supplement due to its powerful anti-oxidant properties, and is often included in skin conditioning face masks. Aim to eat at least one papaya per week

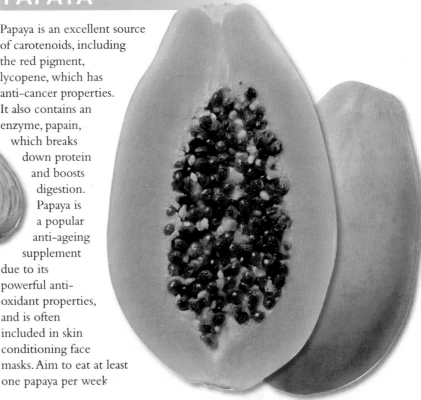

>>

PEPPERS

Capsicum peppers are an excellent source of vitamin C, carotenoids and bioflavonoids. Weight for weight, red peppers contain three times as much vitamin C as citrus fruits do (green peppers have over twice as much). Aim to eat peppers at least three times a week – add them to your salads regularly.

SEEDS

Seeds (eg sesame, sunflower, pumpkin, evening primrose, linseed) are rich in selenium, vitamin E and zinc, which protect us against free radical attack and boost immunity, plus essential fatty acids which help to oil our skin, hair and joints from the inside. Aim to eat a tablespoonful a day sprinkled on salads, vegetables and cereals.

SOYBEANS

Soy and soy products (eg tofu, miso, soya flour, soy sauce) are rich in phyto-oestrogens – weak, hormone like substances that help to prevent ageing due to hormone imbalances. Isoflavones help to keep your skin looking young after the menopause, and can improve menopausal symptoms, endometriosis, benign breast disease and fibroids as well as protecting against breast cancer. Ingesting as little as 60gm per day may be enough to provide these benefits. Soy milk is also available to use as an alternative to dairy milk in tea and cooking.

TOP SUPERFOODS FOR YOUR HEART

- fish
- almonds
- garlic
- citrus fruit
- olive oil
- tomatoes
- dark chocolate
- wine
- chillies
- tea

SWEET POTATOES

As a good source of anti-oxidants, which include carotenoids and vitamins C and E, these orange-fleshed sweet potatoes are a very valuable addition to your diet. Carotenoids will help to protect you against age-related loss of vision, as well as helping to protect the skin from sun damage. It is believed that they may also protect against a number of cancers. You should aim to eat sweet potatoes at least once a week.

TEA

Green, black and white teas are rich in anti-oxidants that reduce the risk of coronary heart disease and some cancers, especially those of the stomach and bladder. Research suggests that those drinking at least four cups of tea a day are half as likely to have a heart attack as non-tea drinkers are and less likely to suffer from high blood pressure. High intakes (eg 8 to 10 cups per day) may reduce the risk of some cancers, especially those of the stomach, colon, rectum, pancreas, breast, skin and bladder.

'Research suggests that those drinking at least four cups of tea a day are half as likely to have a heart attack as non-tea drinkers'

TOMATOES

Tomatoes contain lycopene, an anti-oxidant red pigment that protects against coronary heart disease and some cancers. Cooked tomatoes release their lycopene content best of all, so tomato ketchup, and pizza and pasta sauces are actually the richest dietary sources! You should include tomatoes in your diet every day.

WINE

Many studies show that a moderate intake of alcohol (20-30g per day) is more beneficial for the heart than remaining teetotal. Scientists recently announced in the British Medical Journal that drinking a glass of wine every day (150ml) can cut your risk of getting coronary heart disease by a staggering and satisfying third.

Although they didn't specify the colour, most research shows that red wine is more beneficial than white – especially with meals. Anti-oxidants in the wine seem to protect dietary fats from furring up artery walls and have a thinning effect on blood. Keep intake within healthy limits.

'Scientists recently announced that drinking a daily glass of wine (150ml) can cut your risk of coronary heart disease by a staggering and satisfying third'

YOGHURT

Live bio (biological) yoghurt contains healthy, digestive bacteria that can help to keep the intestines healthy and boost immunity. All yoghurts are made using bacteria, but those in non-bio yoghurt are instantly destroyed by your stomach acid. The bacteria in live bio yoghurts do not get destroyed and grow inside you, inhibiting the growth of bad bacteria linked with peptic ulcers and stomach cancer. Eat live, low fat bio yoghurt (or take a probiotic supplement) most days. The calcium content of yoghurt also helps to build strong bones and prevent osteoporosis.

TOP 10 SUPERFOODS AGAINST CANCER

- broccoli
- sweet potatoes
- tomatoes
- carrots
- apricots
- cherries
- citrus fruits
- grapes
- papaya
- soybeans

FOODS TO AVOID

Just as some foods are good for you, others are bad in excess. In general, these are the foods that you should be wary of:

SALTY FOODS

The link between salt intake and high blood pressure is now strong. By reducing your salt intake from 9g to 6g you can lower your risk of a stroke by 22% and your risk of coronary heart disease by 16%. Most dietary salt is hidden in processed foods including canned products, ready-prepared meals, biscuits and breakfast cereals.

To cut back on salt intake avoid:
- adding salt during cooking or at the table
- obviously salty foods such as crisps, bacon, salted nuts
- tinned products, especially those canned in brine
- cured, smoked or pickled fish/meats
- meat pastes, pâtés
- ready-prepared meals
- packet soups and sauces
- stock cubes and yeast extracts

You should check all product labels and select brands with the lowest salt content.

TIP

When reading labels, those giving salt content as 'sodium' need to be multiplied by 2.5 to give table salt content: eg a serving of soup containing 0.4g sodium contains 1g salt (sodium chloride).

SMOKED FOODS

To help lower your risk of cancer, the World Cancer Research Fund advise consuming cured and smoked foods in moderation. Smoked foods contain chemicals known as nitrosamines which are linked with bowel and stomach cancer.

COVERED IN CHEMICALS

Testing of fruit and vegetables on sale in the UK has found that one third have pesticide residues, many containing four or five and some as many as seven different toxins. Three per cent contain residues above accepted limits, and some imported products even contain illegal chemicals (eg chlormequat, DDT) known to cause tumours in animals. Where possible, choose organic produce.

PAST THEIR BEST

Ideally, consume fresh produce within a few days of purchase for the highest nutrient content – especially of vitamin C. Some vegetables, such as asparagus, lose 90% of their vitamin C content during a week's storage. Once fruit juice is opened, its vitamin C content rapidly falls even when chilled; virtually all is lost within 14 days. Root vegetables (eg potatoes) lose 10% of their vitamin C content per month during storage.

PROCESSED

Cut right back on processed, pre-packaged foods with a high content of polyunsaturated fats, margarine, and vegetable shortening and hydrogenated fats. These contain omega 6 fatty acids which are linked with hardening the arteries.

>>

REVITALISING DIETS

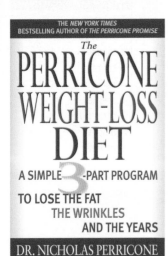

The
**PERRICONE
WEIGHT-LOSS
DIET**

A SIMPLE **3**-PART PROGRAM

TO LOSE THE FAT
THE WRINKLES
AND THE YEARS

DR. NICHOLAS PERRICONE

THE PERRICONE DIET
Dr Nicholas Perricone
(Time Warner Books)

WHAT IS THE DIET?

The Perricone Weight Loss Diet is reported to help you lose fat, diminsh wrinkles and make you look years younger. Said to be a 'facelift in your fridge', the plan revolves around eating anti-inflammatory foods such as salmon, lean turkey, blueberries, salad, oatmeal, green tea, water and olive oils.

These are all foods that avoid bloating and are rich in anti-oxidants and Omega 3. Conversely, you must avoid all processed foods and products containing sugar, as these will cause inflammation, leaving you with saggy, thick, discoloured skin.

By unlocking the link between inflammation and unwanted weight gain, Dr Perricone's diet focuses on the foods, supplements, and lifestyle changes that help you to look younger and accelerate fat loss by increasing metabolism and building muscle mass. Dr Perricone's ideas are explained in three simple steps – firstly by eating the right foods, secondly by taking the correct supplements and thirdly, but most importantly, by making meaningful lifestyle changes to enable you to lose fat and keep it off.

It's a 'facelift in your fridge'

TRIAL

Carole, 44, tested out the Perricone diet for one month

How easy was it to follow?
The program was surprisingly easy to follow. Although the recommended foods are not items I would usually have in my fridge, it was good to try something new and I found all the ingredients easy to incorporate into my diet.

What difference can you see?
After a couple of weeks, my skin definitely looked fresher. I was sleeping much better and had less noticeable bags under my eyes. My hair and nails were shiny and strong, whereas before they were quite brittle. I have also managed to go down a notch on my belt which was an added bonus!

Will you stick with it or never use it again?
There are certainly elements of the diet that I will incorporate into my daily eating plan. I love having lean turkey and fish at most meals and I really enjoyed the healthier snacks. I don't think I'm going to stick to the plan permanently, but I will definitely go back on it for a health boost or if I have a few pounds to shift for a special occasion in the future.

DR. DAY TURNS BACK THE CLOCK WITH A REVOLUTIONARY PROGRAM FOR AGELESS SKIN

Forget the Facelift

DORIS J. DAY, M.D. WITH SONDRA FORSYTH

FORGET THE FACELIFT
Doris J Day
(Penguin Books)

WHAT IS THE DIET?

In Forget the Facelift, American dermatologist Dr Doris J Day promises younger-looking skin without surgery, regardless of your age or the condition of your skin. The diet is a four-step program designed to promote a healthy body and mind.

Step One is the Quick-Start Ageless Skin Care Regimen which promises instant results by making your own cleansers, masks and scrubs at home. Step Two is the Ageless Skin Inner Makeover, where Dr Day lays out her plan for releasing negative emotions and using relaxation to eliminate stress's harmful effects on the skin. Step Three is the Ageless Skin Diet and Exercise Program to help clear the skin from the inside out, including facial exercises that will help prevent the expressions that cause wrinkles to appear.

HARRODS

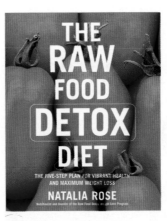

THE RAW FOOD DETOX DIET
Natalia Rose

(Harper Collins)

WHAT IS THE DIET?

The Raw Food Detox Diet is a five-step plan to promote 'vibrant health and maximum weight loss' and is written by nutritionist Natalia Rose. She has abandoned trends for carb counting, calorie counting, and fat-gram counting, instead choosing to focus on the quality of the food itself. Her Raw Food Detox Diet is based on the principle that the secret to optimal health and weight loss is a diet rich in natural, raw foods that not only nourish the body, but help to eliminate years of accumulated toxins that weigh it down.

There are no strict rules and regulations, in fact, you don't even have to eat an all-raw diet to benefit from the plan as there is a range of hot-cooked recipes designed to optimise the nutrients you are getting from your food. The book begins with a quick quiz to determine what transition level is best for you, then offers a range of recipes and techniques for ushering in head-to-toe spring cleaning – with menus designed to deliver extra energy, clear skin, shiny hair and a slim, satisfied body. Natalia explains how your body responds to various foods and food combinations, and puts the science of enzymes to work for you.

For those who feel that they might need a little more help in order to restore their youthful appearance, Step Four details non-invasive treatments such as Botox, Restylane, laser treatments, chemical peels, collagen injections and microdermabrasion.

The book also provides a list of 'skin saboteurs' that readers must avoid at all costs in order to keep their skin healthy and ageless. In addition, you'll find tips for improving your overall appearance, including dress, hair, and make-up tips, which will make the skin look even better.

TRIAL

Sue, 54, spent a month following Dr Day's regime.

How easy was it to follow?
At first, I found making the scrubs and cleansers rather time-consuming, but once they were made, it was really nice to use something so natural on my skin every day. I also had to keep a journal to ensure I was following the skincare regimen – the routine of recording it made it much easier to stick to. The approach was holistic, involving lots of 'inner' cleansing through relaxation techniques which I really enjoyed. I like the fact that this plan focuses on striking a healthy balance between eating well, exercising and taking time to rest and recuperate.

What difference can you see?
Generally, I am feeling much more relaxed, which has made my skin appear more radiant. The recommended foods boosted my energy and the home-made products boosted my skin and circulation so I felt much fresher.

Will you stick with it or never use it again?
I loved the skin-friendly food recipes and will definitely continue to use them. I also think I will make some more scrubs and masks for a weekend treat. I have enjoyed learning the relaxation techniques and will definitely continue to use them, although I will only do the facial exercises when no one is around as I feel a bit silly doing them!

HARRODS

>>

TRIAL

Aline, 39, adopted The Raw Food Detox Diet Plan for one month

How easy was it to follow?

I liked the fact that I never felt deprived, as there was no measuring portions or cutting out any major food groups or anything like that. In fact, I had a very varied diet and the recipes were delicious. The only drawback is that they were sometimes complicated to make.

What difference can you see?

Even without doing any substantial amounts of exercise, I can feel my clothes becoming looser and my body looks quite a lot leaner. I feel a lot lighter and my skin, hair and nails have noticeably improved.

Will you stick with it or never use it again?

This is more like a detoxification program than a diet really, so I think I could probably stick with it as a short-term lifestyle change when I need a health boost. I liked the fact that I could still enjoy rich, satisfying foods, such as avocados, whole-grain pasta, fresh fruit, wine, chocolate, coconut, and even butter, so I did not feel deprived or starved at all.

THE WRINKLE CLEANSE
Cherie Calbom
(Penguin Books)

WHAT IS THE DIET?

Renowned US dermatologist Cherie Calbom has written the Wrinkle Cleanse diet to reveal the nutritional secrets to having fewer wrinkles and firmer, toned skin in just two weeks. Wrinkles, sagging skin, weight gain, memory loss and low energy are the all-too-common signs of an ageing body. By adopting a diet rich in raw foods, vegetable juices, whole grains, and lean protein, Cherie believes you can cleanse your body of toxins and protect yourself from the inflammation and free-radical damage that cause wrinkles and other symptoms of ageing.

The 4-step plan of The Wrinkle Cleanse aims to give you softer, younger-looking skin through a 14-day diet that rejuvenates the cells in your body, stopping and even reversing the ageing process. It also involves a juicing program that cleanses your body of built-up toxins and reduces the appearance of wrinkles and sagging skin, an energy-boosting supplement program to help renew skin and increase vitality, and a cleansing boost program that deep-cleanses your body to keep you on track for total rejuvenation. The book has 75 recipes and helpful menu plans to ensure the proper nutrition for fighting ageing, losing weight, and feeling great at any age.

TRIAL

Helen, 48, tried out the Wrinkle Cleanse program for 4 weeks

How easy was it to follow?

At first the diet plan seemed quite complex, as there were lots of juices and supplements to add into my daily routine. However, I was surprised how quickly I became used to having them and, once I could see the results, cleaning the blender every day no longer seemed like such a chore!

What difference can you see?

As promised, within five days my skin was glowing and my under-eye bags had almost disappeared. The food groups are all anti-oxidants which are supposed to repair skin from the inside out and resist the effects of pollution, and I felt and looked more vibrant.

Will you stick with it or never use it again?

I think the diet is fairly easy to stick to, as it mainly involves eating fruit, vegetables and some protein at every meal, with a daily treat of a dark chocolate bar (which contains flavonoids to boost circulation and collagen production). As the diet is a cleansing one primarily, I don't feel the need to do it all the time but I think I will adopt it for maybe one week a month. I'll also keep up drinking loads of water though, as it has flushed out my system and made my skin look better and less puffy.

A-Z OF ANTI-AGEING SUPPLEMENTS

Although youthful vigour may not last forever, a number of supplements can help to slow down the ageing process, especially anti-oxidants, many of which are now available over the counter and are intended to be taken in addition to your daily diet.

One of the main causes of premature ageing is the action of free radicals, unstable molecular fragments that trigger harmful chain reactions and wreak havoc in the body. Free radicals are largely responsible for the loss of skin elasticity, age spots, wrinkles, hardening and furring up of the arteries, lowering immunity and cancer.

We can't escape free radicals as they are produced by our normal metabolic reactions, as well as exposure to environmental pollutants, cigarette smoke and sunlight. We can minimise the damage they cause, however, if we have enough anti-oxidants on board. Anti-oxidants are our protection against free radical damage, patrolling the body and destroying them.

TIP

Where a wide dose range is given for supplements, start at the lower end for a general benefit. You can work up to a larger amount if you want an increased effect. Doses higher than those suggested here may be recommended by a nutritional therapist, and are best taken only under their supervision.

CAUTION: Do not take supplements during pregnancy except under medical advice.

ACETYL-L-CARNITINE

L-carnitine is a non-essential amino acid made in the liver that is widely present in the diet in small amounts. To receive an anti-ageing benefit, however, a supplement is needed to obtain optimum quantities of it.

WHAT IT DOES
L-carnitine regulates fat metabolism by taking long chain fatty acids to the energy-producing factories (mitochondria) in body cells. The more L-carnitine available, the more fat you can burn.

'Recent research suggests L-carnitine improves memory, energy levels and reduces signs of ageing in animals'

>>

LIFESTYLE

Recent research suggests that L-carnitine improves memory and energy levels and reduces the signs of ageing in animals. L-carnitine and alpha-lipoic acid work synergistically and are often taken together.

HOW MUCH YOU NEED
250 mg to 1g daily.

SIDE EFFECTS/SAFETY
Increased body odour and diarrhoea may occur at very high doses (eg over 4g daily).

ALPHA-LIPOIC ACID

Alpha-lipoic acid (ALA) is a vitamin-like substance produced in small quantities in the body, and is also obtained from the diet, for example in spinach and meats. To get an anti-ageing benefit, however, a supplement is needed to obtain optimum quantities of it.

WHAT IT DOES
ALA acts as a co-enzyme with B group vitamins to optimise energy production in cells. It is a powerful anti-oxidant and regenerates other important anti-oxidants such as vitamins C and E. ALA is mainly used to boost energy levels and combat chronic fatigue, helping to maintain youthful vigour. This is often taken together with L-carnitine.

HOW MUCH YOU NEED
50 to 100mg daily as an anti-oxidant. 100 to 200mg up to three times a day for therapeutic use – eg to boost energy in those with chronic fatigue.

SIDE EFFECTS/SAFETY
Mild skin rashes or gastrointestinal side effects have occurred, but are rare.

CO-ENZYME Q10

Co-enzyme Q10 (CoQ10) is a nutrient that has been found to be beneficial for a surprising variety of health problems. This vitamin-like substance's levels start to decrease after the age of 20 or so, as we slowly absorb less and less of it from our diet and produce less in our body cells. Dietary sources of CoQ10 include meat, fish, wholegrains, nuts and green vegetables.

WHAT IT DOES
CoQ10 is involved in the complicated process of turning food into energy, and it improves oxygen use during this process. As CoQ10 levels fall, cells may not receive all the energy they need, and may age prematurely. CoQ10 also reduces hardening of the arteries and can normalise high blood pressure and improve heart function.

HOW MUCH YOU NEED
Supplements range from 10mg to 100mg daily.

SIDE EFFECTS/SAFETY
No serious side effects are reported, even at a high dose. There can be occasional, mild nausea.

EVENING PRIMROSE

Evening primrose oil is a rich source of gammalinolenic acid (GLA), an oil whose production in the body is easily blocked by dietary and lifestyle excesses.

WHAT IT DOES
GLA helps to maintain a healthy hormone balance, and reduces inflammation. Latest research suggests evening primrose oil can reverse the effects of skin ageing, providing a more youthful appearance within three months with improvements in skin moisture, moisture loss, smoothness, elasticity and firmness.

'Latest research suggests evening primrose oil can reverse the effects of skin ageing, providing a more youthful appearance within three months'

HOW MUCH YOU NEED

1,000mg to 3,000mg daily.

SIDE EFFECTS/SAFETY

Do not take if you have a rare, nervous system disorder known as temporal lobe epilepsy.

FISH OILS

Omega 3 fish oils, which come from the flesh of oily fish (for example, mackerel, herring, salmon, trout, sardines and pilchards), are rich in essential fatty acids derived from the micro algae on which they feed.

WHAT IT DOES

Omega 3 fish oils have a powerful inflammatory action, helping to 'oil' the joints and skin to keep them more youthful. Omega 3 fish oils have a beneficial effect on blood and heart rhythm, helping to reduce the risk of dying from coronary heart disease and stroke.

HOW MUCH YOU NEED

500mg to 4g daily.

SIDE EFFECTS/SAFETY

Seek medical advice before taking fish oil supplements if you have a blood clotting disorder, are taking a blood thinning drug such as warfarin, or if you have diabetes. Also, some people are allergic to fish products. It's also worth mentioning that emulsified oils can help to prevent the 'fishy' after-taste that some people find off-putting.

GINKGO BILOBA

Extracts from Ginkgo biloba leaves have a relaxing effect on blood vessels and a thinning action on blood that improves circulation to the peripheries such as the hands, feet and head. By improving blood flow to the brain, it helps to improve memory and concentration and is also helpful for dealing with depression.

HOW MUCH YOU NEED

120 mg daily, usually best taken in the morning.

SIDE EFFECTS/SAFETY

You should seek medical advice before taking ginkgo if you are taking any blood thinning

treatment such as warfarin or aspirin, although no effects on blood clotting have been found at usual therapeutic doses of Ginkgo biloba.

GRAPE SEED EXTRACT

Extracts from the seeds of red grapes contain proanthocyanidins that act as anti-oxidants which are more concentrated than those found in red wine itself.

WHAT IT DOES

Grapeseed extracts have a beneficial effect on the circulation, reducing the risk of coronary heart disease and stroke. They protect eyes from age-related visual loss and enhance skin smoothness and elasticity.

HOW MUCH YOU NEED

100mg to 200mg daily.

SIDE EFFECTS/SAFETY

No serious side effects have been reported.

'Grapeseed extracts have a beneficial effect on the circulation, reducing the risk of coronary heart disease and stroke'

GREEN TEA

Green tea contains powerful flavonoid anti-oxidants that are at least 100 times more powerful than vitamin C, and 25 times more powerful than vitamin E. While supplements are available, you can drink it. You can mix it with black tea if you prefer a more traditional taste.

WHAT IT DOES

It reduces premature ageing and boosts metabolism to help with weight loss. Green tea extracts are extremely beneficial for all kinds of age-related skin changes.

>>

CHAMPNEYS

HEALTH RESORTS

Get firmer, younger looking skin at Champneys

Our finest ever facial, the Collagen Enriched Anti-Ageing treatment* is available at any Champneys resort (Champneys Henlow in Bedfordshire, Champneys Forest Mere in Hampshire, Champneys Tring in Hertfordshire or Champneys Springs in Leicestershire).

This luxury facial uses traditional French deep brush cleansing, steaming, massage and advanced marine collagen face and eye masks, which leaves your skin firmer and plumper with fine lines reduced - perfect for mature skin or for those wishing to prevent the signs of ageing.

To book your stay or day visit www.champneys.com

Or call reservations on 08703 300 300

Champneys - voted Health Plus magazine's 'Best Rejuvenating Break' in its 2005 Anti Ageing Awards
*Not an inclusive treatment.

In fact, they are added to a variety of skin care preparations because of their healing qualities.

HOW MUCH YOU NEED

500mg daily.

SIDE EFFECTS/SAFETY

No serious side effects have been reported.

ISOFLAVONES

Isoflavones are weak, oestrogen-like plant hormones found in members of the pea and bean family, such as soybeans and chickpeas.

WHAT THEY DO

Isoflavones provide a useful hormone boost when oestrogen levels are low after the menopause, helping to maintain moist, smooth skin. Isoflavones also have beneficial effects on the circulation and bones.

HOW MUCH YOU NEED

2.25mg to 50mg isoflavones daily. 60 grams of soy protein provides 45 mg isoflavones.

SIDE EFFECTS/SAFETY

None reported in adults.

'Isoflavones provide a useful hormone boost when oestrogen levels are low after the menopause, helping to maintain moist, smooth skin'

LUTEIN

Lutein is an anti-oxidant carotenoid pigment which cannot be made in the body. Good dietary sources include yellow-orange and dark green fruit and vegetables, such as sweetcorn, pumpkin, spinach and broccoli and kiwi fruit.

WHAT IT DOES

Lutein is an important supplement for healthy vision, protecting against cataracts and age-related vision loss. It is often commonly referred to as 'nature's sunglasses'. It is thought that high intakes of lutein may decrease the risk of coronary heart disease and lung cancer.

HOW MUCH YOU NEED

A typical dose is 2mg to 6mg daily, often as part of a mixed carotenoid supplement. Alternatively you could include kiwi fruit and broccoli in your diet two or three times a week.

SIDE EFFECTS/SAFETY

No significant side effects reported. High doses may cause temporary (and harmless) orange-discolouration of the skin.

'Nature's sunglasses, lutein helps to prevent age-related eye problems'

LYCOPENE

Lycopene is a red carotenoid pigment that is found in foods such as tomatoes, pink grapefruit, papaya and watermelon.

WHAT IT DOES

Lycopene is increasingly recognised as protecting against coronary heart disease and cancer. Lycopene is depleted in skin exposed to ultraviolet light, suggesting it plays a role in protecting the skin from sun damage.

HOW MUCH YOU NEED

Typical doses are between 5mg to 15mg daily, or you could eat tomatoes most days (the good news is that cooked tomatoes in pizza sauce and ketchup are among the richest sources!).

SIDE EFFECTS/SAFETY

No significant side effects have been reported.

MILK THISTLE

Milk thistle seeds contain a unique mixture of anti-oxidants known as silymarin, the most active ingredient of which is silibinin.

WHAT IT DOES

Silymarin helps detox liver cells and may help the liver to metabolise oestrogen more efficiently.

It is also used for improving skin cell production and promoting fresher, brighter, clearer skin.

HOW MUCH YOU NEED
70mg-200mg silymarin three times a day, preferably between meals.

SIDE EFFECTS/SAFETY
May cause a mild laxative effect due to increased production of bile.

PYCNOGENOL

Pycnogenol is an extract obtained from the bark of the French maritime pine. It contains a rich blend of anti-oxidants that make it 50 times more powerful than vitamin E, 20 times more powerful than vitamin C and 16 times more active than grapeseed extracts.

WHAT IT DOES
Pine bark extracts have a beneficial effect on circulation, reducing the risk of coronary heart disease and stroke. It is widely taken to treat conditions associated with poor circulation, including the prevention of deep vein blood clots on long haul flights.

HOW MUCH YOU NEED
50mg to 200mg daily.

SIDE EFFECTS/SAFETY
No significant side effects have been reported.

REISHI

Reishi, or red Ganoderma lucidum, is known as the 'mushroom of immortality' in China.

WHAT IT DOES
Reishi has been used for over 3,000 years to enhance energy levels, boost immunity, promote vitality and longevity. Research suggests it lowers blood pressure, promotes sleep and may protect against cancer.

HOW MUCH YOU NEED
500mg two to three times daily.

SIDE EFFECTS/SAFETY
Occasional diarrhoea, skin rashes or mouth ulcers during the first week of taking reishi. Seek

medical advice before combining it with any prescription drugs.

'Research suggests reishi lowers blood pressure, promotes sleep and may protect against cancer'

SELENIUM

Selenium is an essential trace element with an anti-oxidant effect in the body. The richest dietary sources are Brazil nuts and seafood.

WHAT IT DOES
Selenium is a central part of the body's main anti-oxidant enzymes. It helps to protect against a wide variety of degenerative diseases such as hardening and furring up of the arteries, cataracts, arthritis, stroke, heart attack and cancer. Selenium is one of the main anti-oxidants protecting skin from sun damage, and can reduce the formation of age spots.

HOW MUCH YOU NEED
Supplements supplying 100mcg to 200mcg (ie 0.1mg-0.2mg) have significant protective effects against cancer.

SIDE EFFECTS/SAFETY
A limit of 300mcg (0.3mg) daily is suggested. Toxicity occurs above 800mcg (0.8mg) daily.

'Selenium is one of the main anti-oxidants protecting skin from sun damage, and can reduce the formation of age-spots'

VITAMIN A AND RELATED CAROTENOIDS

Vitamin A is obtained either as pre-formed retinol (found in animal fats, meats, liver, kidneys, fish oils, eggs and dairy products) or as carotenoids (yellow-orange pigments derived from dark green leafy vegetables and yellow-orange fruits).

WHAT IT DOES
Vitamin A is a powerful anti-oxidant that regulates how genes are read to produce body proteins.

It is essential for normal growth, sexual health, fertility and youthful vigour. In the eye, vitamin A is converted into a pigment known as visual purple (rhodopsin) which is essential for sight. Several studies suggest that natural dietary intakes of betacarotene and vitamin A are important in reducing the risk of coronary heart disease and a number of cancers. Whether supplemental forms can do the same remains unclear.

HOW MUCH YOU NEED

The European recommended daily allowance for adults of vitamin A is 800mcg (0.8mg) per day.

If vitamin A supplements are used, they are best limited to less than 1.5mg per day although intakes of up to 3mg are considered safe.

Around 6mg should be taken daily as part of a mixed carotenoid intake (eg from five servings of fruit and vegetables per day).

SIDE EFFECTS/SAFETY

You should avoid supplements containing vitamin A during pregnancy. Supplemental forms of beta-carotene are best avoided by those who smoke. Excess carotenoids cause a yellow-orange discolouration of skin, although this is not considered harmful and resolves itself when intakes are reduced.

VITAMIN C

Vitamin C – ascorbic acid – is a water-soluble anti-oxidant. Dietary sources include berry fruits, kiwi fruit, capsicum peppers and citrus.

WHAT IT DOES

Vitamin C acts as an essential co-factor for at least 300 metabolic reactions. It is essential for making collagen, the main substance promoting youthful skin and suppleness. A number of studies show that vitamin C also helps to protect the body against coronary heart disease and cancer.

HOW MUCH YOU NEED

Europe's recommended daily allowance for vitamin C is 60 mg, which is widely considered to be too low. 120mg–250mg vitamin C is a good basic intake. Higher doses of 500mg to 1g vitamin C daily are used as supplements.

SIDE EFFECTS/SAFETY

If you are prone to recurrent kidney stones, restrict your daily vitamin C intakes to no more than 100mg. Larger doses may trigger indigestion or diarrhoea, in which case switch to non-acidic mineral ascorbates. Individuals with iron-storage disease (haemochromatosis) should not take vitamin C supplements except under medical advice. Those choosing to take very high dose supplements should reduce their vitamin C intake slowly over a few weeks rather than stopping suddenly.

'A number of studies show that vitamin C helps to protect against coronary heart disease and cancer'

VITAMIN E

Vitamin E is a group of eight closely related anti-oxidants. The most active form is d-alpha-tocopherol, found in wheatgerm oil, avocado, nuts, seeds and oily fish.

WHAT IT DOES

Vitamin E acts as an anti-oxidant protecting body fats from certain kinds of damage. It strengthens muscle fibres, boosts the immune system, protects against coronary heart disease and improves skin suppleness. Researchers reviewing over a dozen studies involving centenarians have suggested that vitamin E is the key to their longevity; healthy people who survive into their 100s appear to have exceptionally high amounts of vitamin E in their blood compared with those found in younger adults.

HOW MUCH YOU NEED

The EU recommended daily allowance for vitamin E is 10mg.

SIDE EFFECTS/SAFETY

High dose vitamin E is best taken together with other anti-oxidants, such as vitamin C, mixed carotenoids and selenium. Vitamin C is vital to regenerate vitamin E after it has carried out its anti-oxidant function.

WATER

The human body is made up of 60–70% water, and drinking an adequate amount of fluid – around two litres (6-8 glasses) each day – is essential to keep it hydrated. A recent survey undertaken by the Expert Group on Hydratrion revealed that 62% of people are not drinking the recommended amount. This insufficient water intake can bring symptoms such as headaches, cystitis, kidney problems, increases in blood pressure, digestive problems, loss in concentration and lethargy. When we are dehydrated wrinkles become more evident, cellulite worsens and hair loses its shine. Drinking water enhances the skin's elasticity and helps it to retain mositure – when skin gets dry, it is better to reach for a drink than a pot of moisturiser to hydrate from the inside.

Ensuring you consume the recommended two litres a day need not be a difficult task. Whether mineral water, tap water or the slightly sparkling variety, make sure you keep a cup or bottle of water by you each day at work or home and fill it up at 1–2 hour intervals. Drinking more is far better than not drinking enough. Experts say that you would have to drink over 10 litres a day to do any damage to your body – and it is highly unlikely an individual could consume anywhere near this amount!

ALKALINE IONISED WATER

For the extra-health conscious, invest in a filter to remove the impurities from tap water, or even try out the new trend for alkaline ionised water, which has been reported to alkalise your body, provide additional oxygen and act as a new anti-oxidant. Be warned, however, that you need to drink ionised alkaline water over many years to reap the health benefits.

Regular exercise is essential in boosting your fitness level, preventing obesity and giving you youthful vigour

exercises
TO BEAT THE SCALPEL

A YOUNG APPEARANCE is dependent not only on your face, but also on your body. Regular exercise is essential in boosting your fitness level, preventing obesity and giving you youthful vigour. It is also a great outlet for stress, leading to good skin oxygenation (making your skin more radiant and even in tone) and boosting energy levels.

Exercise promotes the release of mood-lifting hormones called endorphins, which help to create a positive mood and outlook. Stress is one of the biggest contributing factors to the onset of ageing skin, so any positive way you can find to deal with it will be beneficial.

Exercise also helps you sleep more soundly and speeds up cell activity and blood circulation so that oxygen and nutrients are delivered to your skin more efficiently. This makes your skin firmer, brighter and better nourished. In her book 'Forget the Facelift', dermatologist Doris J Day also shows that perspiration is the body's waste-removal system, so when we sweat we are clearing all the toxins out of our system. This is another excellent reason why we should all be doing regular exercise.

It can be difficult to find time for exercise, though, so personal trainer to the stars, Joanna Hall, gives you her top tips for body toning exercises you can do in the comfort of your own home to keep you looking trim and youthful.

THE BODY

It's always important to ensure your muscles are warmed up before exercising. You should take a brief 20-minute walk before starting or do some simple stretches. Go through these exercises 3-4 times a week to see maximum results. The whole routine should only take 30 minutes

PROBLEM AREA:

SAGGING BOTTOM

SOLUTION: REVERSE TABLE LIFT

HOW MANY?
Repeat the whole thing 8 times on each leg

1 Start by lying flat on your back on the floor, your spine relaxed and knees bent. Position your feet far enough away from your bottom so you just start to feel your toes come off the floor. Pull down through your belly button, so your tummy muscles are contracted before you start to lift.

2 Slowly lift your bottom up, peeling your back off the floor one vertebra at a time. Start off slowly and use your abdominal muscles to create the movement. You should now only have your feet and shoulders in contact with the floor and your body should be in a straight line from knees to shoulders. This is the bridge position.

3 Extend one leg straight – the knees should still be together. Lift the leg from the hip, pointing the toe. Then lower it so the knees are level again.

4 Repeat step 3 four times then lower yourself back to the bridge position. Slowly peel back down to the floor one vertebra at a time, again using your abdominals to control the movement. Repeat the exercise on the other leg.

Joanna says: 'One of the best bottom firmers I know, great for a pert bum'

PROBLEM AREA:

FLAT BOTTOM

SOLUTION: LEG RAISE

HOW MANY?
Try for 10 repetitions on each side, slowly building to two sets of 10 repetitions

FLAT BOTTOMS

Many of us worry about having too big a bum, but losing weight suddenly can give you a flat bottom that needs plumping!

1 Kneel down on all fours, with your knees and elbows on the floor and your back as straight as possible.

2 Keeping your leg bent at the same angle, raise one knee towards the ceiling so that it is in a straight line with your spine. Slowly push your foot up to the ceiling in short 'pulsing' movements. Aim for 10 repetitions.

PROBLEM AREA:

SAGGING BREASTS

SOLUTION: PUSH-UP WITH LEG LIFT

HOW MANY?

You should aim to do 16 on each side

Joanna says: 'This will not only help to tone the bust line but will also improve posture'

1 Get into a push-up position with arms more than shoulder-width apart and back, hips and legs aligned. Bend your elbows out and lower your chest toward the floor.

2 Lift your right leg more than a foot off the floor as you press back to the start. Repeat, raising your left leg as you push up.

PROBLEM AREA:

BAGGY BELLY

SOLUTION: MOVING DEAD BUG

HOW MANY?

You should aim to do 10 on each side

1 Start by lying down with your back flat on the floor, your feet off the floor, knees bent over hips, lower legs parallel to the floor and your hands directly over your shoulders.

Joanna says: 'This move tones and flattens the whole of the tummy region without putting any strain on the neck'

2 Slowly lower the same leg and arm towards the floor. Gently 'kiss' the floor with your heel and slowly lift your arm and leg back up to the starting dead bug position. Make sure you lower your arm and knee at the same speed to avoid placing any strain on your back.

BAGGY BELLIES

Although unhealthy living can contribute to baggy bellies, most women get them after giving birth.

PROBLEM AREA:
LOVE HANDLES
SOLUTION: TOWEL OBLIQUE REACH

HOW MANY?

You should aim to do 8 on each side

LOVE HANDLES

You probably think of men when you think of love handles – but women have to watch out for them too!

1 Take a large towel and roll it into a sausage shape. Lie on your side, placing your hip on top of the towel. Make sure your hips are stacked up on top of each other and pull in your abdominals tightly to avoid toppling either forwards or backwards. You may need to play around with the towel position so you can use your waist muscles more as you lift.

2 Extend your lower arm along the floor and your upper arm in front of you. Keeping the waist long, stretch out from the top of your head as you lift your body up sideways. You should feel your waist muscles tightening. Slowly lower yourself back down.

Joanna's top tip: 'The arm on the floor is for support and balance – try to avoid using it to push you up'

PROBLEM AREA:
FLABBY ARMS
SOLUTION: CHAIR TRICEP DIP

HOW MANY?

You should be aiming for 12–16 slow repetitions on each side

1 Start sitting on the edge of a chair, with your hands grasping the front edge of the seat. Your fingers need to be facing forward. Slowly move forwards until your elbows are in line with your hands.

2 Support your weight and lower yourself down for a tricep dip position, keeping the elbows pointing back behind you, then go back up.

3 Then, press your hips forward and stretch one arm up over your head on your diagonal before returning to your starting position.

'Your fingers need to be facing forward'

LIFESTYLE

PROBLEM AREA:
OUTER THIGH
SOLUTION: CAN OPENER AND EXTENSION

HOW MANY?

Aim for 12–16 slow repetitions on each side

1 Lie on your side, knees bent as if sitting on a chair. Keeping your feet and knees together, lift your feet off the floor. This is your start position.

2 Keeping your feet together, open your top knee as wide as possible using your outer thigh.

3 Lower your top knee and extend your leg down the length of your body. Bring your leg back into the bent leg position and repeat.

Joanna's says: 'This exercise streamlines the outer hips and thighs and helps to lengthen and tone the muscles of the whole leg'

PROBLEM AREA:
FLABBY INNER THIGH
SOLUTION: INNER THIGH CHAIR SQUEEZES

HOW MANY?

You should aim to repeat this 16-20 times

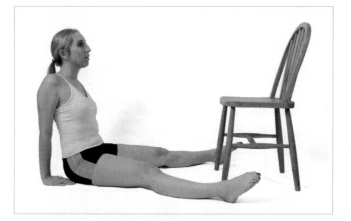

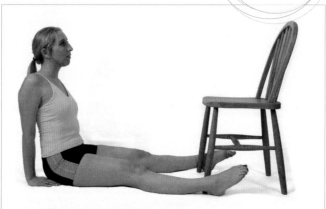

FLABBY THIGHS

Flabby thighs are easy to ignore, hidden under clothes, but they need work too!

1 Sit on the floor with your back straight and legs out in front of you. Have a chair positioned by your feet. Place one leg on either side of the outside of the chair.

2 Press your legs together and focus on pressing from the inner thigh. Hold this for 10 seconds and release.

For more information and helpful fitness tips, go to: www.joannahall.com

THE FACE

The exercises that follow may seem a little unfamiliar, as they all involve working out with your face. Go through these exercises 3-4 times a week to tone your facial muscles with optimum effect, making your skin feel more supple and vibrant and keeping your face looking younger and brighter than ever

PROBLEM AREA:

FOREHEAD

SOLUTION: FOREHEAD PULL

WRINKLES

It's definitely worth giving this simple exercise a try to help keep any lurking wrinkles at bay!

HOW MANY?
You should hold the position for 5 seconds and repeat it once

1 Put one hand on your hairline above your eyebrows and pull gently upward. Then try to pull the muscle upward on its own.

2 When you master this exercise, hold it for five minutes. Relax. Repeat it once.

'This exercise will help to iron out unsightly creases and frown lines on the forehead'

PROBLEM AREA:

EYE

SOLUTION: WIDE EYE ROLL

HOW MANY?
You should aim to hold each position for 5 seconds

'This exercise should help your eyes appear wider and more open'

1 Open your eyes as wide as possible and hold for five seconds. Relax and repeat.

2 Open your eyes wide again and roll your eyes to the left. Hold for five seconds. Relax and repeat. Repeat rolling your eyes to the left, upward and downward. These motions should help your eyes appear wider and more 'open'.

LIFESTYLE

PROBLEM AREA:
FLABBY CHIN AND NECK
SOLUTION: SMILING SWAN

HOW MANY?
You should repeat this exercise 5 times

SMILE!
Smiling and laughter are often said to be the best therapy, and it's true – they stretch your chin muscles!

1 Stand up straight and lengthen your neck like a swan. Break into a huge grin so that you are stretching the muscles of your chin and neck. Hold for five seconds. Relax and repeat this five times. This exercise will help the chin and neck appear tighter and tauter and can also improve the appearance of fine lines around the mouth.

'This exercise will help the chin and neck appear tighter and tauter'

PROBLEM AREA:
JOWLS ON THE THROAT
SOLUTION: JOWL-BUSTER

HOW MANY?
You should aim to do the backwards move twice and the side ones once for each side

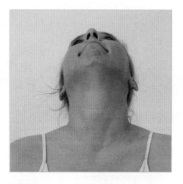

1 Raise your chin, tilting your head back as far as possible. Hold for five seconds. Relax and repeat once.

2 Then raise your chin, tilting your head to the right. Relax and repeat. Do the same on the left-hand side. This exercise will tone up loose jowls.

'This exercise will help to tone up loose jowls on the throat'

TONING YOUR MUSCLES
It might seem odd to do exercises for the face and neck, but it makes perfect sense. As we age, our muscles become weaker and the skin over them begins to sag. By keeping the facial muscles in shape, we can keep our faces looking younger and brighter as well. You can do these exercises in the comfort of your own home, maybe in the shower, or while you're doing the washing up!

OTHER EXERCISES

Holistic exercises are another fantastic way to tone and tighten the body. We round up the best toning and firming exercises to keep you looking radiant and youthful and more refreshed than ever...

YOGA

WHERE TO GO?
The largest yoga organisation in the UK is the British Wheel of Yoga, at www.bwy.org.uk

What is it?

Yoga involves a type of exercise that promotes balance, co-ordination, flexibility, and meditation. Practising yoga regularly can create flexibility, build strength, and develop stamina. Favoured by many over-40 celebrities, yoga creates a leaner, stronger body if practised regularly. Yoga is simple to practise in the comfort of your own home as you do not need any space or special equipment, and sessions can easily be slotted into your everyday routine. By bringing the body into balance, yoga has a positive effect on mental well-being: it helps people to relax, improves concentration, reduces stress and calms the mind. Specific breathing exercises can either stimulate or pacify your mind, helping you to sleep better.

'By bringing the body into balance, yoga has a positive effect on mental well-being: it helps people to relax'

GOOD FOR

- posture
- circulation
- flexibility
- enhancing the functioning of the respiratory and digestive systems
- stress
- concentration

It's reported that it's also good for:
- headaches
- back pain
- anxiety
- menstrual cramps

'Yoga involves a type of exercise that promotes balance, co-ordination, flexibility, and meditation'

INSTANT FIX

CHECK YOUR POSTURE

Good posture is not only good for your muscles, it benefits all your organs – including your skin – and promotes good circulation. Follow these five simple steps for better posture:

1 Sit up as straight as possible when seated for long periods of time. Make sure your seat is adjusted to suit the curvature of your spine and your feet can be positioned flat on the floor.

2 Push your chin back, as this will push your shoulders back and straighten your spine.

3 Pull down the shoulder muscles in your back.

4 Contract your abdominal muscles to pull your stomach in and support your back.

5 Imagine someone is tugging upwards on a string that is attached to the top of your head; this will cause you to stand or sit tall, stretching out vital muscles.

PILATES

What is it?

Pilates is an innovative exercise method that realigns and balances your body by focusing on the core postural muscles that keep the body balanced and support the spine.

Pilates increases flexibility, co-ordination and stamina while promoting maximum muscle strength which will make you both slimmer and fitter. All exercises can be done at home on a mat or towel, so can easily be practised in the comfort of your lounge. As with yoga, if you are trying pilates for the first time, always start with movements for beginners, as learning correct form and alignment are essential for getting maximum benefit as well as preventing injury.

WHERE TO GO?
The Body Control Pilates Association is a leading Pilates organisation at www.bodycontrol.co.uk

GOOD FOR

- decompressing your joints
- stimulating and improving circulation
- better posture
- a stronger back
- a flatter, more toned stomach
- flexibility
- stiffness and soreness of muscles
- especially good for back pain

'Pilates increases flexibility, co-ordination and stamina at the same time as promoting maximum muscle strength'

TIBETAN YOGA

WHERE TO GO?
The largest yoga organisation in the UK is the British Wheel of Yoga, at www.bwy.org.uk

What is it?

Tibetan yoga is a rejuvenating form of yoga, which involves large amounts of meditation. This technique has been shown to stimulate the secretion of anti-ageing hormones and regenerating, health-enhancing chemicals from the brain. Research has proved that melatonin and seratonin (which are thought to be connected to seasonal affective disorder and depression) are increased by meditation, while the stress hormone cortisol is decreased. People who do meditate also secrete more of the alleged youth-related hormone DHEA (dehydroepiandrosterone) than those who don't – in fact, meditating 45-year-old females have an average of 47% more DHEA than non-meditators. Meditation combined with yoga will help revitalise the body from outside and within.

If you're feeling more active, why not combine these exercises with one or more of the following:
- a brisk walk to work
- tennis
- swimming
- taking up an exercise class you enjoy

After all, a lack of exercise will lead to poor circulation and sallowness in your skin, fat accumulation on the chin and jowls and a bloated appearance. Now, where are those trainers?

GOOD FOR

- stress
- memory
- sexual function
- immune defences
- mood
- weight

'Research has proved that the calming hormones melatonin and seratonin (which are thought to help reduce the effects of depression) are increased by meditation'

The most noticeable sign of ageing in hair is the loss of colour caused by a slow-down in the production of a pigment called melanin. Grey hairs usually start to appear by the age of 40, and statistics show that half the population's hair will be 50% grey by the age of 50

your hair
BOOSTING SHINE AND VITALITY

A FULL HEALTHY HEAD OF hair is synonymous with youth and vitality, but as we age our hair naturally loses colour, volume and shine. Consequently, the need to take care of the hair and its style becomes increasingly important as the years pass. Fortunately, the vast and ever-expanding selection of treatments, products and expert advice means hair care doesn't have to be a slog.

COLOUR ENHANCEMENT

The most noticeable sign of ageing in hair is the loss of colour caused by a slow-down in the production of a pigment called melanin. Grey hairs usually start to appear by the age of 40, although some women will go grey much younger. Statistics show that half the population's hair will be 50 per cent grey by the age of 50.

The production of melanin is determined by genetic factors, so your parents' hair will give you an idea how quickly and at what age your own hair will change colour.

Women with blonde hair usually have the best deal in the ageing process as grey hair tends to fade in with the natural colour. While red hair tones down to shades of brown, grey amongst dark hair can be more noticeable. We look at how to choose the right colour later in this section.

GROW THICKER HAIR

As well as losing colour, hair also becomes finer and drier with age. This again is down to the slow-down in the production of melanin which also makes hair soft, flexible and supple. Follicles start to produce hair that is finer and shorter with less volume and density, causing hair to appear thin and dry.

Hair loss is another sign of ageing and, between the ages of 40 and 50, women may lose about 20 per cent of their hair. And while hair loss can occur at any stage of a woman's life for many reasons, including stress, pregnancy, thyroid problems and extreme dieting, it is also a normal part of the ageing process.

Many women will experience hair thinning just before the menopause, known as androgen dependent alopecia (female pattern hair loss). This is due to a natural decrease in oestrogen levels. However, in order for gradual hair thinning to occur, there has to be a hereditary predisposition which can be passed on from either sex parent. Female pattern hair loss is the most common hair loss affecting approximately 60 per cent of women by the age of 50.

Many oral contraceptives and HRT preparations contain the male hormone progestogen which can also adversely affect hair. To maintain healthy hair, you should eat a balanced diet of protein, good carbohydrates, vitamin B12, zinc and iron.

This section explains what happens to hair as we age and provides an in-depth analysis into the products on the market. It also includes advice from renowned hairdressers on choosing the right colour, cut and style to flatter your face and skin type.

USING HAIR DYES

While colouring hair poses no risk for most, some dyes can cause allergic reactions. You should always seek advice if you are worried. Most vegetable dyes (made from plants like saffron and camomile) will wash out of hair and are harmless. Synthetic dyes fall into four categories:
- temporary dyes wash out quickly
- semi-permanent wash out after 6-8 shampoos
- permanent oxidation dyes need an oxidising agent (eg hydrogen peroxide)
- quasi-permanent dyes are a mix of semi-permanent and permanent

---

YOUR GUIDE TO THE BEST HAIR CARE AVAILABLE >>

"I feel **special** because they speak to me in **my language**"

If you need to make a claim, would you want to speak to someone who will understand your needs? To get the feeling, there's only one number to call.

24 hour multi-lingual helpline

BUPA
International

Call +44 (0) 1273 208181
www.bupa-intl.com

REDISCOVER YOUR NATURAL COLOUR

Colouring grey hair is one of the best ways to look younger, but a lot of debate surrounds when to start using dyes, which shades to choose and whether to opt for home colouring or professional treatment

COMMITTING TO COLOUR

Hair colour is about how you feel. You should only colour your hair when you feel ready, and not before. If you're having colour done for the first time, the most important thing you have to think about is your ability to commit to it. It can feel dreadful to commit to a major change in colour, only to wish you'd thought it through more carefully after the event. It's always advisable to go to a professional hair salon when you first decide to colour your hair, so you can get advice from an experienced professional.

Whether darker or lighter shades are better for you depends on your hair and skin tone. Generally, as you age your skin tone softens, and this is usually best reflected in the colour. Don't forget that if

you have the tendency to flush this needs to be considered in the final colour choice.

If you're struggling to find a good colourist for your initial consultation, one of the easiest ways to do so is by simply asking your friends.

HOME TINTING

If you decide to colour your hair at home, it's vital to follow the instructions carefully. If you don't follow instructions properly in terms of development time and the product is removed too soon, you risk ending up with glowing brassy tones. The classic assumption made is that if colour is on for less time, it will be less permanent. This is completely inaccurate, and patchy colour often results if people try to use only one box for their entire head of thick waist-length hair.

Nonetheless, some people do have great results from home colour. For example, stylist Nathan Walker has some clients at Trevor Sorbie who keep their base colour maintained at home, and see him just three or four times a year to get some high or low lights added.

Some home colourants promise to blend current and coloured hair as well as covering grey in 10 minutes. The thicker formulas and specialist application brushes are designed to make the application process simple as well as producing professional-looking results.

James Brown, Clairol's Creative Director says: 'Blending between the roots and previously

'Keeping up with the trends in hair colour will instantly make you look younger, and having a colour that you really like that works for you will give you the confidence to feel younger'
Caroline Shepherd, hairdresser

FROM GREY TO GREAT – ADVICE FROM TREVOR SORBIE

- It's a good idea to hide the first few grey hairs with a vegetable or semi-permanent colour in the same shade as your natural colour, which will last 6–8 shampoos, gradually washing out.

- If you have 50% grey hair, use a longer-lasting semi-permanent colour that fades after around 20 shampoos.

- Disguise 75% of grey hair with a mixture of high and low-lights. Go for lighter shades on the darker sections, or warmer shades on the lighter sections. This can only be done at a salon and will need redoing every 3–4 months.

- To replace colour completely, use a permanent colour that grows out and needs to be retouched every 4–6 weeks. Choose a shade that is slightly lighter than your original shade to avoid any hardness.

Clairol's nice 'n easy root touch-up promises results after only a 10-minute application

>>

coloured hair can be tricky. There are lots of things to watch out for, such as colour dripping on to the rest of the hair, leaving the colour on for too long or not long enough.'

It's important to concentrate on the most visible areas of hair and think about how you wear it. Is your parting to the left or right? Do you tie your hair back in a ponytail? Focus on these areas to achieve the best results.

CARE FOR YOUR HAIR

Whatever you do, don't colour your hair without considering how to care for it. Over 40 per cent of dye sold is specifically developed for covering grey, which – while cosmetically masking grey hair – does nothing to address its specific care and styling needs. Your care regime is as important as your colour choice and you should use a moisturising shampoo and conditioner specifically designed for coloured hair.

TRY IT!
Trevor Sorbie Professional Colour Preserve shampoo (£3.99 for 250ml) and Trevor Sorbie Professional Colour Preserve Riche Conditioner (£4.49 for 250ml)

'Whatever you do, don't colour your hair without considering how to care for it'

ADDING VOLUME

Good products are vital for restoring moisture and volume to any hair, particularly for women as they age. Fine hair needs extra special care, and thinning strands can make hair more difficult to style

TRY IT!
The Trevor Sorbie Professional Rejuvenate range is specifically designed for fine and thinning hair and comprises 10 shampoo, conditioning and styling products

This range is designed for thinning hair

SKINCARE FOR THE SCALP

Another product you could try in order to thicken up your hair is Nioxin from Research Laboratories, described as 'skincare for the scalp'. The three-step salon-only system contains co-enzymes, essential oils, protective herbs and botanicals to cleanse, soothe and moisturise as well as creating the best growing environment for stronger, thicker, healthier hair. Nioxin have a wide range of products, all specifically designed to help your hair look its best.

TRY THE HAIR DOCTOR

Philip Kingsley, who is also known as 'the hair doctor', has a range of thickening shampoos and conditioners as well as the Elasticizer, which is an intensive moisturising treatment for improved stretchability, strength and shine.

Nioxin has a wide range of haircare products

ANTI-AGEING

For added luxury try the Caviar Anti-Ageing Collection from Alterna, a hair care range designed to restore moisture and elasticity and keep hair in top condition. Alterna's exclusive Enzyme therapy ensures the ingredients are absorbed deep into the hair to restore shine and condition.

THICKENING POWDER

An alternate method of thickening hair is the White Cliffs Hair Studio's Toppik powder. Charged with static electricity, the powder-like tiny fibres are applied to dry hair and bond tightly, staying in place during the day and night. This works well for people who still have a fair amount of hair. Toppik hair fibres also stay on in the rain and shower without smearing or dripping.

THICKENING SHAMPOOS

Good thickening or volumising shampoos can rectify the problem of thinning hair by restoring the hair's inner structure with keratin to heal the hair from within. They also cleanse away styling product debris on the outer layer of hair, creating fullness and volume.

'Alterna's exclusive Enzyme therapy ensures the ingredients are absorbed deep into the hair to restore shine and condition'

DEALING WITH HAIR LOSS

Hair loss is, unfortunately, a common problem amongst older women as well as men. It can be embarrassing to discuss, but it shouldn't be pushed to one side, as there are products at hand that can help to prevent it

GROW A FULLER HEAD OF HAIR

According to a study by Top Santé magazine in 2005, six in 10 women will experience hair loss in their lives.

As a prevention for the initial stages of hair loss, the White Cliffs Group recommends Laser Phototherapy. Their Laser Comb is a breakthrough in the treatment of problem hair that uses the energising effects of Laser Photo Therapy to make hair thicker, fuller and softer, used in conjunction with Minoxidil and the supplement HairScripts Complete.

Minoxidil was originally used as a medicine to treat high blood pressure but while using it, some patients experienced hair growth as a side effect. Since then Minoxidil has become a popular treatment for hair loss. It is safe, and does not require a prescription. It works by increasing blood flow and partially enlarging miniaturised follicles. This prolongs the growth phase of the hair cycle, allowing the hair to become longer and thicker. Bear in mind that it may take several hair growth cycles before maximum potential hair growth can be achieved.

The HairScripts Complete supplement, however, works in a different way to Minoxidil.

The White Cliffs Group's Laser Comb is a breakthrough in treating hair loss

BEFORE

AFTER

WHITE CLIFFS GROUP

>>

'Plenty of celebrities wear wigs and you might not even know it. Take Raquel Welsh: she looks fantastic and she has her own range of wigs.' Royston Blythe, celebrity hairdresser

>> CASE STUDY

Catherine Bourcier, now 34, began losing her own hair at the age of 17 and credits the White Cliffs System for restoring her confidence and making the difference between staying in or going out: 'The hair systems are life changing and my hair looked so natural from day one that I never felt self-conscious.'

It blocks the male hormone dihydrotestosterone (DHT) from attacking and shrinking hair follicles, and provides essential vitamins and minerals.

HAIR REPLACEMENT

If hair loss is at an advanced stage, the above treatments may not be effective, but surgical hair replacement has come a long way in recent years and could be the perfect answer.

The White Cliffs' 'ultra custom' hair replacement systems for women make it appear as though the hair is growing right out of your scalp. The hair is woven into a fine net, which is attached to the scalp with an adhesive and can stay on for up to four weeks. Hair can be worn down or tied back away from the face and looks totally natural.

Whether you have lost hair, have thin hair or simply don't like your natural hair, you shouldn't be afraid of wearing hair extensions or seeking advice about wigs. Wigs have come a long way, are easy to wear and can retain a natural look.

HAIR STYLES

It can be hard to figure out what style is right for you, especially if you're surrounded by magazines and adverts showing off hair in a million different styles. We ask the professionals what their advice is...

LOOK LIKE YOURSELF

A lot of debate surrounds how women should style their hair as they get older and whether it should be long, short, curly or straight. While there are some general guidelines when it comes to hair styles for older women, it really depends on the individual. Having a cut that makes you feel more confident will almost certainly make you look younger, and it's all about having the right attitude towards your image. Remember: what suited you 20 years ago may not suit you now.

WHAT MAKES A GOOD CUT?

Fabulous hair can make you look 10 years younger – but what constitutes a good cut? Celebrity hairdresser Royston Blythe tells us:

- As you get older it's important to have movement and body at the crown.
- Hair that is too long and straight can look too thin on an older woman and, equally, hair that is too short can look too harsh and butch.
- Medium length hair can be dressed up, tucked behind the ears or set in rollers for extra body and femininity. Look at Jane Fonda, she's a great role model.

'For shorter cuts I believe that feathering onto the face is extremely flattering. Avoid any harsh haircuts with strong lines. The more mature woman should avoid scraping longer hair back off the face as this will show all natural ageing flaws' Trevor Sorbie

'People say when women hit 40 they shouldn't have short hair, but I disagree and think it really depends on how you look. Lifestyles have changed and women aren't old when they're 60 any more. If a 60-year-old comes into my salon I'm not going to give her a 60-year-old hair cut, I'm going to make her look her best' Royston Blythe, celebrity hairdresser

STAY IN STYLE
Midlands Hairdresser of the Year, Lawrence Anthony, tells us how hair changes as we age

AGE v STYLE

30s 40s 50s 60s

ROBERTO AGUILAR

The thirties is a busy stage of life. Many women may have had, or be thinking of having, a family, and may want to opt for a great-looking style that's easy to maintain. New mums may also need to use a strengthening shampoo to build up their hair post-baby.

Oestrogen levels in the body change with age, and hair does not grow at the same rate as it once did, leaving it starting to thin and harder to style.Women in their forties should have short layers around the face to frame their features.

Women in their fifties whose hair has turned (or is turning) grey and whose skin has lightened in tone should consider having highlights done. Putting highlights through the hair will help to create a more flattering, natural colour.

Women in their sixties choosing a new style should go for shorter cuts and crops. These will help to create the illusion of volume and body, and you should try using a body building shampoo too. There's no excuse for neglecting your hair, no matter what your age.

introduction to

ways to rejuvenate mind and body

FEELING GOOD AND AT ease with yourself can make a huge difference to your life and how you look. There are lots of natural ways to boost your self-image and improve your overall sense of well-being. When you feel happy on the inside, it will show on the outside. Turn the page and read on to find out how.

ALCOHOL: FRIEND AND FOE

A glass or two of red wine can help keep the heart healthy and lower stress levels, but drinking more accelerates the ageing process

Government guidelines suggest women should drink no more than two or three units of alcohol a day (no more than 14 per week), with at least one day each week to be kept alcohol-free.

● One unit is a small glass of low-strength wine, half a pint of weak beer or one pub measure of spirits (25ml).

● Regularly drinking more than this, and binge drinking especially, increases the likelihood of illnesses associated with ageing, from heart disease, stroke, and liver or kidney damage to breast cancer and osteoporosis.

● Heavy drinking ages the complexion because it increases the production of free radicals while depleting the body of anti-oxidant vitamins and minerals essential to skin health.

● Though drinking might make us dozy enough to snooze on the sofa, it reduces deep sleep and leads to early waking, both of which take their toll on looks, immunity, memory and energy levels.

● The liver is a vital cleansing organ: if it's not working well, skin tone, texture and colour are affected. Think how a hangover brings with it pallid skin, dehydrated hair, puffy eyes, cracked lips and aggravated acne.

● Happily, the liver has remarkable powers of regeneration, and the ideal way to detox after the Christmas party season or summer holidays is to say no to alcohol for a week or two.

WHY A LITTLE CAN BE BENEFICIAL

Despite alcohol's ability to age us, a little every day may be more healthy than none at all: several studies associate one or two small glasses a day with a lowered risk of coronary heart disease and Alzheimer's. Red wine contains cell-protecting anti-oxidants called polyphenols found in no other form of alcohol.

'Heavy drinking ages the complexion because it increases the production of free radicals, while depleting the body of vitamins and minerals'

Several studies claim that one or two small glasses of wine a day may be more healthy than none at all

THE AGEING EFFECTS OF SMOKING

Aside from a multitude of other health risks, smoking is also one of the most effective ways to age skin, and yet so many of us can't seem to stop

● Warnings on cigarette packs make clear the link between smoking and disease (smokers in their 30s and 40s are five times more likely to have a heart attack than non-smokers).

● Smoking is also the second most effective way to age skin after sun exposure.

● Smoking creates free radical molecules, held responsible for 80 per cent of skin ageing. Moreover, smokers have lowered levels of the anti-oxidant vitamins needed to mop up the damage. Nicotine constricts blood vessels, reducing oxygen and nutrient flow and lessening the blood's ability to carry away toxins.

● This all leads to wrinkles and the grey, pale complexion doctors refer to as 'smoker's face'.

● In addition, smoking thickens elastin, produces a collagen-destructing enzyme, and decreases oestrogen, all detrimental to plump, elastic skin. Pursing the lips to inhale and squinting against the smoke exacerbate the damage.

● Inhaling on a cigarette pumps pesticides, heavy metals, sweeteners and additives into your system.

● The smoke poisons your home, too, collecting in dust and carpets ready to assault your skin in drying air pollution long after you finished the cigarette.

HOW TO STOP

Tobacco is addictive, and research suggests women find it harder to quit than men. Firstly, you must decide you want to stop (not just cut down). It may help to record your reasons in a journal so you can keep reminding yourself of them. Then:
● enlist the support of family, friends and your GP
● ask about specialist clinics or groups
● check with your doctor before buying off-the-shelf products (for example, patches, gum, inhalers)
● use appropriate nicotine replacement therapy or non-nicotine Zyban tablets to reduce your cravings. They're most effective for those who crave a cigarette on waking.

● Call the NHS Stop Smoking Line (0800 1690 169) or Quitline (0800 002200).

KEEP UP THE GOOD WORK

Try not to put yourself within reach of temptation. If you usually hang out with smokers, suggest meeting instead at a cinema or no-smoking restaurant. To occupy restless hands, take up knitting or fiddle with worry beads (young Greek women swear by them). Pack your diet with anti-oxidant fruit and vegetables, drink plenty of water to flush out toxins, and visit the gym: a healthy diet and light, regular exercise reduce withdrawal symptoms and boost natural painkillers.

Treats are essential: spend your savings on instant mood-lifters, such as 70% cocoa-solid chocolate, and longer term prizes, like a shoe-shopping or day-spa trip. You might support your effort with natural therapies. The Organic Pharmacy recommends its Quit Smoking Kit (£44), comprising homeopathic and herbal remedies plus anti-oxidant supplements.

TOP TIPS
● Do you crave that first early morning cigarette? Try to change your routine in one of these ways in order to avoid starting the day off with a smoke:
● Why not try to get into a routine of doing exercise in the morning – even a few sit-ups will help discourage you from smoking.
● If you normally linger in the bedroom, why not decide to get straight into the shower right after waking up?
● If you normally have a cigarette over a coffee in the morning, why not try to switch to orange juice instead?

'Research suggests the skin of smokers over the age of 30 ages twice as fast as the skin of non-smokers'

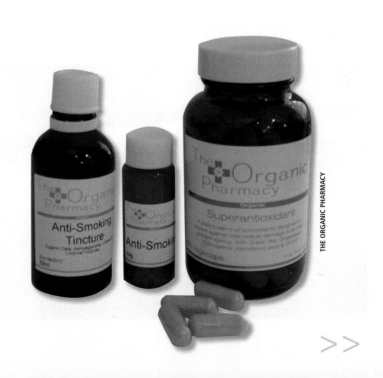

THE ORGANIC PHARMACY

>>

SOOTHING OILS

● **Chamomile**
Soothes the mind and works on both the muscles and nervous system to relax the body, thus promoting restful sleep

● **Jasmine**
Soothes anxiety, calms nervousness, and promotes restful sleep

● **Lavender**
Soothes anxiety, reduces stress, and promotes restful sleep

● **Neroli**
Lifts depression and confidence, soothes anxiety, combats nervous tension, and promotes restful sleep

● **Sandalwood**
Comforts the nerves, eases tension and anxiety, and promotes restful sleep

Note: always read the dosage and contraindications on the bottle of essential oil before use. If you are at all unsure as to the suitability of any essential oil, consult a qualified herbalist or a doctor for advice. Do not use essential oils if you are pregnant unless it is with the express permission of your medical practitioner or midwife. Always dilute essential oils in a base oil, such as sweet almond oil, before use (the usual ratio is 2 drops of essential oil per 5ml/1tsp base oil, but be sure to check the bottle first).

FIND WAYS TO DE-STRESS YOUR LIFE

We all need a little stress to drag ourselves out of bed in the morning and meet work deadlines, but too much or continual stress is ageing

The biochemical changes caused by stress hormones age the body and brain. At times of stress, blood rushes to muscles away from the vital organs and brain to prepare the body to tackle the source of stress. Heart rate and blood pressure increase, and breathing becomes fast and shallow. When this state of readiness is not released in an appropriate way, many body systems suffer: one study suggests the process may age blood vessels, other research maintains that prolonged exposure as we age decreases the size of the hippocampus,

the part of the brain involved in memory and emotions. Negative states of mind that come with stress, such as anger and anxiety, can derail well-being and may prompt lifestyle choices, from smoking to binge-drinking, that further fuel the ageing process. And, of course, the effects of stress show in the body and face. Clinical studies show stress hormones worsen skin conditions. Tension gathers around the neck and shoulders. Time will etch these tensions into the body, unless you take steps to counter them.

NATURAL WAYS TO COUNTER STRESS

REDUCE MONDAY STRESS

Those who thrive on stress tend to use positive ways to cope with its impact. Some of us, however, are not so lucky. Researchers tell us that Monday is the most stressful day of the week, with the risk of stroke higher than on other days. So, easing yourself into a new week will help preserve your health and good looks. Why not have a lunchtime top-to-toe makeover or treat yourself in some other way, to make Mondays easier on yourself?

EXERCISE

30 minutes' activity undertaken on most days of the week is a supreme stress-buster. Exercise strengthens the bones and immune system, boosts oxygen intake for youthful-looking skin, and helps to keep the emotions level and memory keen, the muscles toned and the joints mobile.

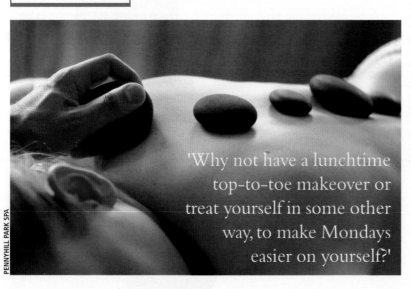

'Why not have a lunchtime top-to-toe makeover or treat yourself in some other way, to make Mondays easier on yourself?'

You don't even have to go to the gym:
- try a brisk lunchtime walk
- use stairs instead of lifts
- cycle to the shops or work
- even active housework and gardening count
- walking is especially good: women who walk regularly seem less at risk of osteoporosis and age-related memory loss.
- Yoga and t'ai chi destress the mind and deepen breathing while strengthening muscles and lubricating joints. Yoga inversions (upside-down poses) are especially good for the face and neck
- For more on yoga and meditation, see page 153

BATHING

Bathing is wonderfully stress-relieving. Soaking in warm water revives aching muscles and joints and promotes blood flow in the skin, allowing take-up of nutrients and removal of waste. It also sedates the nervous system, making worries seem less taxing. Add products blended from essential oils and herbs. Alternatively, you could throw four bags of green tea under the hot tap and swish in 8 drops of essential oil of geranium (this should be avoided during pregnancy) mixed with 2 teaspoons of grapeseed oil just before stepping in. Place a cold eye mask or cucumber slices over your eyes to soothe them.

CROWN

CROWN

GET A GOOD NIGHT'S SLEEP

Burning the candle at both ends makes a difference to how you look and feel because sleep is the ultimate anti-ageing treatment, and we all suffer without it

Sleep is a time of repair and renewal: trials show that patients who sleep best recover most quickly from surgery. Human circadian rhythms (our internal body clock) are modulated by the changing light of dawn and dusk, with our differing drives – one striving for wakefulness and the other moving toward sleep – governing different times of day. Late nights and the concept of a twenty-four hour culture override this balance (as does caring for newborns!). But, if we upset it continually, equilibrium and our looks will suffer. Less than six hours' sleep a night regularly brings under-eye bags, grey-looking skin, lank hair, a bad temper and reduced dynamism.

'Less than six hours' sleep a night regularly brings under-eye bags, grey-looking skin, lank hair, a bad temper and reduced dynamism'

>>

SNACK TO SLEEP

● About an hour before bed, eat a light snack rich in the amino acid tryptophan, which helps reduce anxiety and promote relaxation

● In a 2005 study, mild insomniacs who did this reported more restful sleep and increased alertness next morning.

● Good snacks include a small chicken, tuna or egg sandwich on wholemeal bread (carbs promote sleepiness), a banana, glass of milk, oat cake or handful of almonds or sunflower seeds.

● A wind-down routine from early evening can be helpful. Try to exercise during the day and avoid caffeine and tannin (in tea) from late afternoon.

● Declutter the bedroom, removing sources of mental stimulation, including laptops and televisions, and make the bed with crisp, clean linen.

● Write down worries and to-do lists in a book, then wipe them from your mind.

● Relax in a warm bath, swishing in 10 drops of essential oil of lavender (avoid during pregnancy).

● Practise breathing exercises or listen to calming music.

● Read a book until your eyes start to close.

Long-term sleep deprivation is linked with depression, depleted immunity, greater risk of heart disease and even increased mortality. One study implicates sleep loss in obesity: it boosts an appetite-stimulant chemical and reduces levels of a blood protein that affects how full we feel.

Simple sleep-promoters

● Between 35–50 sleep becomes more shallow, so you may need to rethink your bedtime.

● The amount of sleep you need is enough to leave you refreshed and ready-to-go. Experiment with bedtimes before you find a routine (lack of routine upsets the body-clock) and, regardless of sleep quality, rise at the same time daily.

● Try a daytime nap if you can: research suggests napping between 2pm–4pm from your 50s can boost brain performance.

● If a medical or emotional issue is feeding your insomnia, consult your GP.

'A wind-down routine from early evening can be helpful. Try to exercise during the day and avoid caffeine and tannin (in tea) from late afternoon'

SELF-IMAGE

While looking good is important to women of all ages in today's society, what matters more is feeling good about yourself from the inside. When we are happy within ourselves, this radiates outward, affecting our moods, relationships, work, home life and – of course – our looks. When you feel content and confident, your self-esteem and self-respect are boosted. Being strong and happy emotionally cannot be fixed with a scalpel or face cream and that is why it is so important for our well-being. A strong sense of self is something that cannot be created externally – we need to develop it ourselves.

Whilst cosmetic treatments can make a difference to the way you look, they are not a cure-all. Cosmetic treatments and products may make you feel happier about your looks and, as such, boost your confidence, but they cannot fix underlying emotional problems in your relationships or work life.

It is important to embark on surgery with a level head – if you are feeling low or vulnerable, surgery may make you feel worse rather than better. Instead of looking to a surgeon for a cure,

you need to reaffirm your own sense of self and reassess what you want in life to boost your self-esteem, self-confidence and self-respect. In the pages that follow, we look into ways to boost a positive self image, so that you radiate happiness and confidence from the inside out.

POSITIVE APPROACH

Growing older gracefully is an achievable goal for any woman. By adopting a positive, mature approach to ageing, you will feel more comfortable in your own skin and more optimistic about the future. It is possible to stay young at heart without emulating the clothes, fashions and behaviours of teens! By adopting a positive, youthful attitude to life, you will find that worries and concerns evaporate and you will be able to adapt to becoming older, rather than living in fear or denial. Look at all the positives that come with age rather than focusing on what you miss about your youth. As one patient who went for a face lift consultation says: 'I considered having everything lifted and smoothed, but then thought, no, I've earned these wrinkles. Every laughter line has a story behind it and I love having a face that is etched with experience and character, rather than a blank canvas.'

What counts isn't your chronological age but how you feel. You must try not to look back at what you once were with regret – it's important to enjoy who you are now. You must be prepared to change your attitudes to ageing and realise that becoming older doesn't have to be a negative thing.

'When you feel content and confident, your self-esteem and self-respect are boosted. Being strong and happy emotionally cannot be fixed with a scalpel or face cream and that is why it is so important for our well-being'

Look forward to all the surprises and experiences the future has in store. It's true what they say: age really is just a number.

ACCEPTANCE

Unfortunately, we live in a judgemental society. Magazines are littered with images of stick-thin 20-somethings in bikinis. The good news is that this vision of beauty is not what most people actually desire. Having curves and wrinkles are all part of life, and you need to enjoy them rather than hide them. By adopting a positive attitude to your looks and accepting you'll never look as good in a bikini as you did at 21, you can learn to make the most of what you have now. All women can look good at any age – it is simply about enhancing your good features, rather than focusing on your problem areas. Most women fear their looks and sexual allure will fade with time, but acknowledging that you are still a desirable woman with attractive qualities, no matter what your age, will make you more appealing. It's time to stop apologising for not being a supermodel and enjoy your body. A woman with body confidence and a great attitude to her looks is far more desirable

'Life is 10% what happens to us and 90% how we react to it. Realise you have choices and how good it feels once you start making the right ones'

than one who focuses on her negatives. Chances are, no-one will even notice your wobbly thighs unless you insist on pointing them out.

NEW GOALS

A great way to adapt to ageing is to establish new goals. As you become older, rediscovering your identity and personal values is key. While you are defined to some extent by your work, family and relationships, it is important to also maintain a strong sense of personal identity. Have ideas, interests and values that are your own and invest in them. It is important to take stock of all your achievements and the skills and qualities you have developed over the years - and to also keep developing yourself and look for new interests to pursue. As you become older, you have more liberty to look after yourself and meet your own needs without feeling selfish. Go on – spoil yourself!

DAVID WIGMORE

TOP TIPS FOR BEATING THE BLUES WITH LIFE COACH LIZ WILDE

Exercise: Liz Wilde says: 'Researchers in the US found that when women over 40 undertook an exercise program for eight weeks, 50% reported a decrease in menopausal hot flushes and headaches, 40% a decrease in stress and anxiety, and 30% reported an increase in energy and sex drive. Time to dig those trainers out!'

Make positive decisions: 'Just understanding your belief system is negotiable (ie realising you're not locked in for life) can totally change your perspective. Life is

10% what happens to us and 90% how we react to it. Realise you have choices and how good it feels once you start making the right ones.'

Indulge: 'For an instant lift, take some time out to do something you enjoy every day. Whether it's having a long bath, reading a magazine or some retail therapy: taking time to indulge yourself leaves you feeling happy, relaxed and positive.'

Affirmations: 'Every day we put blocks in the way of achieving

what we want. From "I'll never get the promotion" to "I'm too old to go back to college", these are hurdles we've created to stop ourselves achieving our goals. Change this to "I will get the promotion" and "I will go back to college" and see things happen. An optimistic attitude breeds positive outcomes.

Socialise: 'When you're feeling down, it's easy to turn into a hermit but spending time with people you love will boost your mood. There's no better way to resolve worries than to share

them with a friend to get things in perspective.'

Set your goals: 'Clarity is power – the clearer the picture, the more motivated you will feel and the easier it will be to achieve your goal. Do one thing a day to bring you closer to your goal. It's easy to feel overwhelmed if you only look at the big picture. Breaking things down into small steps will make them feel far more achievable.'

For more top life coaching tips from Liz Wilde, visit: www.wildelifecoaching.com

>>

SPEND TIME OUTDOORS

● Natural light increases serotonin in the brain for instant positivity and stress reduction. A daily ten-minute sun bath is no longer a skincare no-no. Studies show a little sun exposure (before 10am or after 3pm) may even safeguard against skin cancer. Basking in the sun helps the body create vitamin D, essential for healthy bones, strengthens immunity and may lower cholesterol.

● Being surrounded by greenery can reduce nervous and muscular tension and promote calm positivity. In hospital trials, patients who contemplated nature reported less anxiety and pain and healed more rapidly. Fill your space with indoor plants like the common peace lily, spider plant and Boston fern which cleanse the atmosphere of skin-ageing pollutants released from electronic equipment and vinyl-based carpet, wallpaper and paint.

LAUGH AND SMILE THE YEARS AWAY

Laughter relieves stress and stimulates the immune system – even the smallest smile can help roll back your biological age

People who consider themselves happy have one-tenth the rate of serious illness and early death than unhappy people. Those content with a close circle of family and friends feel younger and live longer – ten years longer, says an Australian study. Simply looking at photographs of happy, familiar faces reduces stress, suggests other research. If you feel mildly blue, try these self-help strategies. If you feel down most of the time, talk to your GP.

ACT HAPPY

Smile in the morning to stimulate painkilling, immune-boosting brain chemicals. Studies suggest even pretending to be happy is effective. Smiling exercises the facial muscles; laugh, too, and you boost oxygen flow. Thinking positive reduces negative thought patterns that age us prematurely by influencing behaviour and lowering self-esteem. Start each morning with a positive affirmation: 'I am strong', 'I can be happy', 'I will feel positive all day' and in time your horizons will broaden as you start to believe it. The act of utterance itself is beneficial: bring your breathing in sync with the phrase, then slow it down, feeling the repetition still and centre you. Medical studies show that chanting lowers blood pressure and heart rate and promotes alpha brain waves responsible for a relaxed body and quiet, alert mind.

SLOW DOWN TO ENJOY LIFE

● knock off work early if you can reasonably do so
● spend a day shopping at the start of the season to spoil yourself
● catch the matinee of a new show without feeling guilty about it
● if you feel trapped in an overwork culture, reassess your options: might job-sharing, working part-time, or freelancing from home help you regain a sense of pleasure in your daily life?
● at home, turn off the PC, mobile and TV to counteract our culture of speed and worry
● read or doze in a hammock
● walk the dog
● cook from scratch
● you might take up a new hobby, like painting, or join a choir, dance or writing group

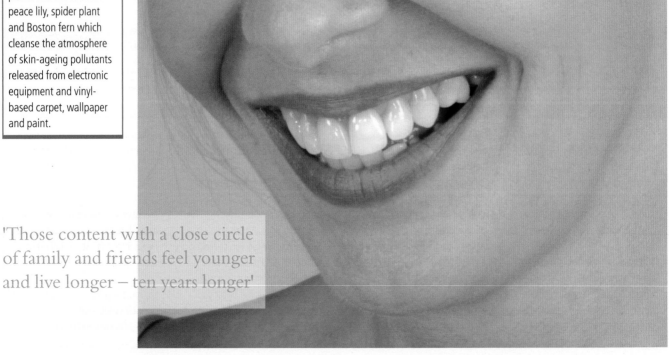

'Those content with a close circle of family and friends feel younger and live longer – ten years longer'

NATURAL ANTI-AGEING TIPS

Boost your sense of well-being naturally with techniques that relax and rejuvenate mind and body simultaneously

Bringing the body and mind into equilibrium strengthens our innate healing powers, and enables them to resist ageing influences such as stress and air pollution more successfully.

The most important weapon in the natural anti-ageing armoury is deep breathing. When we hunch over a desk or slump on the sofa, the shoulders clamp forward and the chest collapses. Aside from being bad for our posture, this restricts the in-flow of energising oxygen for cell repair, and impedes a full exhalation of toxins. Breathe fully and you empower the body's natural anti-ageing defences, while quieting a restless mind. As well reading about the topics that follow, you can also turn to page 153 for more on meditation and yoga.

TREAT YOUR FEET

A foot massage or pedicure melts tension in the face and results in better circulation. Because the soles of the feet contain nerve endings and pressure sensors connected to every part of the body, reflexology treatments may help rejuvenate many body systems. You can get similar effects from walking barefoot over uneven ground. In China and Japan this form of exercise is practised to enliven the body, awaken the senses and keep the mind youthful. Studies at the Oregon Research Institute report that walking for 30 minutes daily over cobbles lowers blood pressure and improves balance as we age.

DEEPENING THE BREATH

● Sit comfortably upright. Close your eyes and notice your breath moving in and out.

● Inhale to a count of four, feeling your abdomen expand and rib-cage widen.

● Exhale for four, sensing your abdomen draw toward your lower back and shoulders relax. This is one cycle.

● Repeat the cycle 12 times, feeling the count naturally become slower. If this feels comfortable, start to extend the out-breath, without forcing, until you are breathing in for four and exhaling for eight.

TAKE A SAUNA

● Finnish women attribute their fabulous skin, youthful good looks and peace of mind to regular saunas.

● Spending slow time relaxing with friends in a dry-heated room scented with birch leaves will do more than just easing aching muscles and cleansing pores.

● Health benefits come as blood vessels expand to increase oxygen and nutrient supplies to the skin and to flush away toxins. The immune system and kidney function are strengthened, blood pressure is lowered, and changes in the brain heighten a sense of peacefulness.

GOODSHOOT

'Bringing body and mind into equilibrium strengthens our innate healing powers, and enables them to resist ageing influences more successfully'

>>

LIFESTYLE

BOOST YOUR WELL-BEING

Complementary therapies are no longer being viewed with scepticism, and having acupuncture or reiki will help you feel rejuvenated

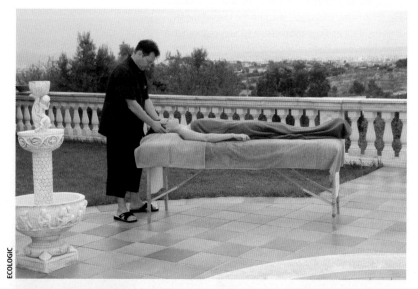

ECOLOGIC

DID YOU KNOW?

● Reiki is a generic word in Japan, and is used to describe many types of healing and spiritual work.

● Although it is thought that Reiki originated in Tibet thousands of years ago, and that it contains Buddhist concepts, it is generally agreed that Reiki is religiously neutral.

● Dr. Mikao Usui, a Japanese Christian educator in Kyoto, Japan, rediscovered Reiki and practised and taught it in the mid- to late 1800s.

● The tradition was continued in Japan, and was introduced to the Western world in the mid-1970s. Since then its use has spread dramatically worldwide.

Holistic therapies used to be all about finding the path to enlightenment, but these days ancient techniques are being used as a natural way to boost your sense of well-being and look years younger, without having to resort to invasive cosmetic treatments. Ancient methods of rejuvenation are as popular as ever today – and their enduring appeal suggests they must deliver pleasing results. From reflexology to reiki, there are therapies that relax and revitalise, with most techniques working on the principle that a healthy, happy inside will reflect itself in a glowing exterior – in particular plump, firm and radiant skin. The added bonus is that all of these complementary therapies are safe and natural with no side effects or healing time, so you can have a lean body, shining eyes and great skin with minimal discomfort.

REIKI FACIAL

Reiki is an Eastern spiritual healing technique which uses energy to bring relief of pain and relax the mind, body and emotions. Reiki is purported to release our 'inner flow of energy', to revitalise the body's organs and restore and balance the body, which brings more youthful vitality, improved health and anti-ageing benefits. Reiki is a non-invasive, light-touch technique of energy transfer, transmitted through the palms of the hands, as well as the eyes and breath.

During a facial, a practitioner will use a systematic technique of hand placements that can stimulate energy to certain areas of the body. In releasing 'blocked' energy, Reiki is designed to detoxify and purify the body.

Where to go:
Eve Lom Facial using Reiki techniques: 1½ hours, £110 – Dorchester Spa, The Dorchester, Park Lane, London W1A 2HJ (020 7629 8888) 1-hour Reiki sessions, £90 – The Spa at Pennyhill Park, London Road, Bagshot, Surrey GU19 5EU (01276 486100)

ACUPUNCTURE FACIAL

The facial rejuvenation acupuncture treatment is based on the principles of oriental medicine and involves the insertion of hair-thin needles into particular areas of the face, ears, neck, hands, upper body and legs along channels of energy. Specific points are chosen to stimulate the movement of energy in the body and to forget trouble areas, such as sagging cheeks and bags around the eyes. This is a painless, non-surgical method of reducing the signs of the ageing process and rejuvenating the body, so that you both look and feel younger.

Proponents say the process may erase as many as 5-15 years from the face after the recommended 12 treatments, with results potentially lasting years. Fine lines may be entirely eliminated and deeper wrinkles diminished, bags under the eyes can be reduced, jowls firmed, puffiness eliminated, droopy eyelids lifted and double chins minimised. Other possible results include: more hydrated skin, increased circulation of blood to the face, increased collagen production, better muscle tone, tighter pores, brighter eyes, improved hormonal balance and reduction of stress.

Where to go:
The Oriental Medicine Practice, 35 North View, Westbury Park, Bristol BS6 7PY (0117 907 8890)

AYURVEDA THERAPY

Ayurveda is an ancient Indian therapy that combines herbal medicines, massage and manipulation with yoga, diet and lifestyle advice. Ayurveda is designed to restore balance to the body, to bring about mental well-being and vitality.

Relaxing and rejuvenating treatments such as soothing oil massage (a deep tissue massage to loosen impurities) and herbal steam baths are coupled with yoga sessions and a specifically designed eating plan to get your body into alignment, so that you will appear more youthful and radiant. Reports say that those following an Ayurvedic detox program can lose up to 8kg in six weeks, with clearer skin and bags of energy. In addition, an individualised set of herbs will be prescribed to improve brain function and circulation, reduce stress and promote natural rhythms of activity and sleep. The documented benefits of the program are a reduction in cholesterol, diastolic blood pressure, anxiety levels and levels of toxins.

Deep tissue massages will soothe and relax you, as well as loosen impurities from your skin

Where to go:
Ayurvedic skincare and diet products are available online from www.maharishi.co.uk
A 45-minute Ayurvedic head massage costs £71 from The Spa at Pennyhill Park, London Road, Bagshot, Surrey GU19 5EU (01276 486100)
Holistic Ayurvedic Detox can also be found at the Alive and Well Clinic, 61 Shelton Street, Covent Garden, London WC2H 9HE (020 7379 5531)
www.aliveandwell.co.uk

'Ancient methods of rejuvenation are as popular as ever today – and their enduring appeal suggests they must deliver pleasing results… working on the principle that a healthy, happy inside will reflect itself in a glowing exterior'

PENNYHILL PARK SPA

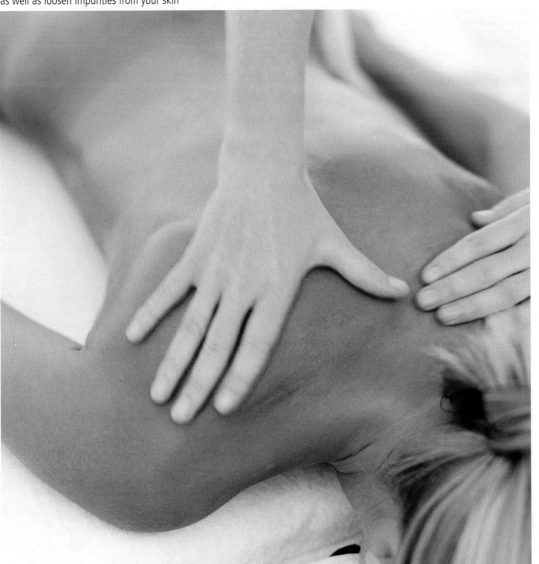

DID YOU KNOW?

● It is believed that Ayurveda was recorded in written form over 5,000 years ago in India, and was said to be a medicine dealing with both body and spirit.
● The earliest sage-physician-surgeons in India (c.2000BC) saw health as an integral part of spiritual life. It is said that they received their training of Ayurveda during meditation.
● The books which contain the original knowledge of the Ayurvedic world are believed to be over 1,200 years old.
● Ayurveda is one of the oldest medical systems in the world.

skin
natural carotenoids &
active plant extracts

hair
vitamins &
cystine amino acid

&nails
magnesium, zinc
& minerals

Why do leading beauty experts and models *use* and *recommend* Perfectil®?

Because Perfectil's unique 'Triple Active' formula is designed for skin, hair and nails, there's no need to take several different supplements. One effective tablet helps safeguard your diet with natural plant extracts including carotenoids, antioxidants and grape seed extract for skin, plus nutrients to provide deep nourishment for hair follicles and at the nail bed. Perfectil® is so complete there's no need to take an additional multivitamin. So as well as pampering yourself on the outside, remember real beauty comes from within.

For further information about Perfectil®, visit www.perfectil.com

Perfectil® TABLETS   beauty from within

From Boots, Superdrug, Holland & Barrett, supermarkets, chemists, Harrods, GNC and health stores.
Those with nutritionally inadequate diets may benefit from Perfectil®. Suitable for vegetarians.

VITABIOTICS
WHERE NATURE MEETS SCIENCE